Who Shall Live?

WHO SHALL LIVE?

Medicine Technology Ethics

edited by Kenneth Vaux

FORTRESS PRESS
Philadelphia

Library of Congress Catalog Card Number 70-99463

2298G69 Printed in U.S.A. 1-251

Contents

Foreword

During the late 1960's, spectacular scientific discoveries and unprecedented medical events gave rise to reconsideration of medical ethical codes. One of these was the successful technical allotransplantation of a human heart. In the ensuing eighteen months, there followed almost 150 such operations, and with them a resurgence of questions about ethical, legal, and moral considerations in medicine. The clinical, moral, ethical, theological, and psychological implications of these questions deserve serious deliberation and analysis, with a reconsideration of our human values and an attempt to arrive at satisfactory moral guidance.

A reclusive life needs few ethical guides; it is communal living that gives a code of ethics real meaning. Human values are shaped in social context. Medical ethics, as an expression of that cultural ethos, seeks to reflect the highest humanitarian and benevolent values. Whether the physician honors the Hippocratic, Nuremberg, or Helsinki formulation, his natural impulse is to alleviate suffering, preserve human life, and enrich man's existence.

Houston's first international conference on Ethics in Medicine and Technology provided a platform for discussion of these vital issues and spotlighted the growing awareness of their importance. It produced no easy answers or premature rules. Instead, it permitted provocative discussion of these issues among leaders in a wide range of disciplines.

It is not possible to formulate a rigid ethical code that will embrace every circumstance and provide definitive moral directives for specific instances. Every medical experiment and every patient must be considered individually. Ethical decisions in medical science must therefore depend finally on the wisdom, integrity, and compassion of the physician and his peers, because these are the qualities that nourish love and reverence for life in our culture.

September, 1969

Michael E. DeBakey, M.D.
Baylor College of Medicine

Introduction

It was only a few years ago that Kenneth Boulding in his study on *The Meaning of the Twentieth Century* suggested that we stand today "at the edge of a biological revolution, which may have results for mankind just as dramatic as the nuclear revolution of a generation ago."[1] In present perspective, his prophetic words seem almost too reserved.

In the months that have followed the Houston Conference on Ethics in Medicine and Technology numerous heart transplants have been performed in an effort to extend the lives of persons otherwise fatally ill. A successful series of operations have been performed by teams at St. Luke's and Methodist Hospitals, just footsteps from the office in which I write. All indications point to the fact that human heart replacement by means of cardiac homotransplantation and artificial implant is indeed widespread and that spare parts exchange in medical care is just beginning.

There are crucial issues connected with these procedures for extending life. But critical concern also surrounds the techniques involving human manipulation and control at the beginning of life. New possibilities of genetic analysis and correction on the scientific side coupled with moral directives such as the recent papal encyclical on human life (*Humanae vitae*) have intensified the ethical concerns that arise at that point. Then there is the whole problem of the creation of living substance: the reduplication of the DNA molecule; alteration of chromosome material; the impending possibility of decoding and generating a developed organism from the information present in a single healthy cell.

---

[1] Kenneth Boulding, *The Meaning of the Twentieth Century* (New York: Harper and Row, 1964), p. 7.

Genetic engineering; eugenics and euthenics; birth control, sterilization, and abortion; life extension; manipulation and control of human behavior through the myriad means now available; euthanasia and the cultural way of death—all linger as problems confronting our society. These problems become acute as our medical ability continues to outstrip our ethical sensibility. The issues are at once specific and ultimate. Each particular question of life extension carries within it the question of life itself. The conference sought to raise the issues and bring them into focus in their profound dimension.

Although there is general public recognition of the urgency of the issues involved, the discussion has yet to move beyond what Dr. Adrian Kantrowitz has called the present "lamentably confused" state.[2] At the disciplinary level the cleavage between the "two cultures"[3] has widened and deepened. Very few centers of scientific research and development are engaged in any depth discussion of these ethical problems. A few medical schools have added ethicist-theologians or philosophers to the faculty, but their influence does not yet run deep.

On the other side of the coin there seems to be an earnest willingness on the part of many scientists and technologists to examine the ethical dimensions of their research, to be engaged in rather than withdraw from the practical implementation of their work, and to be concerned for its social ramifications. The physicists, sensitized by years of dialogue and literature, are not going to forfeit ethical responsibility as did the postwar atomic theoreticians. The life scientists have known in private and public discussion that they are always aware of how close they are to the quick of the humanum and of how great a burden of responsibility this carries.

The Houston conference was convened to give platform to the growing awareness of the importance of these issues. It sought to place the issues in context and to discover ethical directives for specific situations. It also sought to probe the philosophic depth and mystery of the several concerns.

---

[2] Adrian Kantrowitz in U.S., Congress, Senate, Committee on Government Operations, *Government Hearings on National Commission on Health, Science, and Society,* March, April, 1968, pp. 28 ff.

[3] C. P. Snow, *The Two Cultures and the Scientific Revolution* (Cambridge: Cambridge University Press, 1961).

The impetus for the conference came not only from the scientists, but from the medical, social science, and religious communities as well. When the idea was first proposed and support requested, the great oil companies proved as interested as the man on the street. It was no problem to gather the substantial budget and the planning leadership from all segments of society.

The central planning committee included the following distinguished citizens of the Houston community: The Reverend Edwin De F. Bennett, University of Houston; Father Samuel Femiano, University of St. Thomas; The Reverend Don Goodwin, Metropolitan Campus Ministry Association; The Reverend Thomas Cole, Institute of Religion in the Texas Medical Center; The Reverend Arman Jorjorian, St. Luke's-Texas Children's Hospital; Professor Clark Read, Rice University; Father Raymond Haddad, Medical Center Catholic Apostolate; Dean A. A. White, University of Houston Law School; Mrs. Lucile Leon, Texas Women's University; Dr. Dolf Curb, The Diagnostic Clinic; Dr. Harry Lipscomb, Baylor University College of Medicine; Rabbi Henry Tavel, The Jewish Rabbinate; and James Crout, Baylor University. Rice University and the Institute of Religion in the Texas Medical Center spearheaded the administration of the conference.

Our first task was to gather the finest leadership that could be found. Initial encouragement came when we secured as our main speaker the man who has done more work in the field of ethics than any other in history, Helmut Thielicke of Hamburg, Germany. His work in the ethical dimensions of life, developed in his massive *Theological Ethik*,[4] reveals a historic and philosophic depth that is missing in much of the more pragmatic American work.

Knowing that ethical problems can hardly be viewed in isolation, the planners secured Margaret Mead to set the issues in the cultural-anthropological context. No one else in the world could have done this from such a rich background of experiences or provided such a stimulating keynote address to the thousand strong gathered at Rice University.

Emmanuel Mesthene, director of the Harvard Program on Technology and Society, brought a philosophic dimension to the conference with his address on Technology and Values. The dis-

[4] For the volumes of Thielicke's *Theological Ethics* thus far translated see the Bibliography.

cussion during that session was typical of the lively cross-disciplined dialogue and the significant engagement of industry that characterize the speaker's program at Harvard.

Robert Drinan, Paul Ramsey, and Joseph Fletcher directed the conferees' attention to the specific issues of abortion, genetic control, and the use of technological devices in medical care. The presentations and the reactions by university scholars provided concretion and application for the more reflective work of the other presentations.

The nearly 250 delegates that gathered from around the country came from every walk of life. Teachers in medical schools joined law students; nursing directors met campus chaplains with common concerns; industrial planners shared views with local pastors. Indeed, the most significant long-range impact of the conference may well derive from the broad sharing of experience and frank opinion by people whose paths otherwise rarely cross.

The conference anticipated what would become a widespread dialogue in this area. In the past few years numerous committees and commissions have set out to study the ethical problems of medicine and technology. Groups such as the American Medical Association and the American Nurses Association have recently reviewed and revised their pertinent documents. The United States Congress initiated leadership with the hearings on the "Mondale Proposal: Senate Joint Resolution 145," looking to the establishment of a presidential commission on health, science, and society. Several interdisciplinary research teams are now at work on theoretical aspects of the problems, and more sharing and discussion among the healing team is found in hospital corridors.

The level of discussion of the ethical issues, however, is popular but lacking in depth. The literature in the field is spotty and shallow. Research on the ethical problems in no way parallels the intensity or significance of the accelerated biotechnological research. The field is one which calls for continuing systematic study. Isolated conferences, occasional articles, and sporadic collections of papers are not enough. There is great need for high quality research that builds on what has been done before. I have selected a basic bibliography for inclusion in this book in order to provide a launching pad for the increasing number of scholars who will hopefully be giving more time, perhaps even concentrated professional attention to these problems.

The conference only raised and refined many of the questions, acknowledging that solutions and guidelines will take longer to discover. It had numerous significant consequences. At the stimulus of conference delegates many other medical centers have held similar symposia. Several research projects have been launched. Indeed, under the direction of philosopher Daniel Callahan an international research center for the study of ethics, society, and the life sciences has been established. It is now quite clear that an international forum of concerned life scientists will emerge to articulate the same ethical imperatives that the physicists, for example, have expressed in the *Bulletin of Atomic Scientists.*

It appears as if we stand at the threshold of an exciting era. Perhaps we are leaving the age of enamoration with things and moving into an age of fascination with the things of the human spirit. Perhaps, as the Surgeon General has suggested, we are beginning to concentrate more on the quality of life as opposed to an orientation merely in terms of quantity. As James L. Dennis, Director of the University of Oklahoma Medical Center, has said: Our attitude may be shifting from a concern for "more to live longer" to a concern for "more to live better."[5]

In this book we have sought to shape the varied facets of the Houston conference into an integral whole. The reader will find in each chapter, in addition to my own brief Introduction (set in italics), one of the major conference presentations (slightly edited, particularly through the provision of footnotes) plus excerpts from the ensuing discussion. Our purpose has been to point up the myriad problems as well as the ethical options. We have sought to heighten sensitivity, explode simplistic answers, enlarge the field of vision, and undergird the work of those who seek to keep life on earth human. Our hope is that the volume will be disturbing to the many who still claim that there is no problem.

Kenneth Vaux

[5] James L. Dennis in U.S., Congress, Senate, Committee on Government Operations, *Government Hearings on National Commission on Health, Science, and Society,* March, April, 1968, pp. 247 ff.

Who Shall Live?

Part One

THE CONTEXT

1. The Cultural Shaping of the Ethical Situation

We are coming to see more and more how broadly based are the ethical problems of medicine and technology, and how wide a range of considerations interweave to create the fabric of the ethical context. The cultural setting is critical in any thoughtful evaluation of ethical decision-making. It was for this reason that Dr. Margaret Mead was invited to deliver the keynote address of the conference.

Dr. Mead is widely acknowledged to be among the most eminent of the world's cultural anthropologists. Her distinguished career of research and teaching has produced many pioneering syntheses and analyses (some of her pertinent writings are listed in the Bibliography). After distinguished professorships at Harvard, Columbia, and Yale, she now serves both as Curator of Ethnology at the American Museum of Natural History and as director of an experimental educational program at Fordham University. In the summer of 1966 she made yet another significant contribution to the study of the formation of human values at the intersection of technology and society when she chaired a section of the Geneva Conference on Church and Society sponsored by the World Council of Churches, where attention was focused on many of the concerns of the Houston conference.

One of the themes introduced by Dr. Mead was to reverberate through many of the sessions. She spoke of the attitudes we have toward technology and technologists, and toward our own fellow men, as our lives are increasingly shaped by the new discoveries in sophisticated technology. This theme later emerged with power in Professor Thielicke's contrast between technological titanism and an attitude of responsible reverence with respect to one's ability to subjugate the environment. The conference highlighted the importance of a sober attitude that refuses to succumb either to despair and nihilism on the one hand or to naive progressivism on the other. If there was a consensus discernible at all in the several discussions it would be that man must energetically pursue his destiny to build the earth, and that his attitude must hold in constant juxtaposition the relentless abandonment to truth that generates discovery on the one hand, and the awesome responsibility that this freedom entails on the other.

Margaret Mead's remarks, as always, covered a wide range of subjects. On the surface one may wonder what the new morality, the right to vote, urban riots, Vietnam, and sex have to do with the overall theme. As the conferees reflected on the conference, however, they found great value in the breadth of her presentation. She spoke of an attitude—an attitude of trust in the healers of our society—and she spoke of a mood —a mood of realistic optimism transcending the despair and nihilism that can so easily set in as one is faced with the overwhelming problems raised by medicine and technology. More profoundly, she set the problems in a framework embracing both the total fabric and culture and the continuum of history. This expansion of horizon served both to refine and to focus the complex field of concern to which the conference then addressed itself.

Lively response to Dr. Mead's address came from the reactors, Dr. Edward Norbeck, Professor of Anthropology at Rice University, and Dr. Richard Evans, Professor of Psychology at the University of Houston.

The Cultural Shaping of the Ethical Situation[1]

Margaret Mead

An anthropologist can make two contributions to a discussion like this. Initially, he can help to place any contemporary discussion of ethics in the long-time span of human evolution, concerning which we know a certain amount and have done a certain amount of work. Secondly, he can place the discussion strictly in the contemporary situation, within American culture of the present day, a culture which is itself to be seen within the framework of worldwide culture and within the context of our whole long and varied religious history.

[1] Edited from the transcript of an address given without a text, on March 25, 1968.

The Broader Context

As nearly as we can tell, human beings from the time that we are willing to call them humans—which is, of course, a rather personal choice at the moment—have had the innate capacity to tell good from evil. Now this can be described as a fall or a rise, depending on how you wish to take it. It does not change the phenomena in the least that there seems to have been a point, whether of many years' or of an instant's duration in human history, when man became capable of discriminating between good and evil. Of course, what has been called good and evil has varied enormously, but the belief that some things are good and some evil is found in every human society.

It is often wrongly asserted that when we anthropologists observe that Eskimos let their grandmothers die, we mean that it is all right to kill grandmothers. What we do say is that under the circumstances of primitive Eskimo life it was ethical for a grandmother to elect to die because she was endangering the future of her children and her grandchildren, and it was not unethical for the sons and daughters to co-operate with her ethical choice. We say too that any society that is capable of keeping grandmothers alive but instead refuses to give them teeth and lets them die is strictly unethical.

So the content and the conditions differ but not the basic ethical choices. Similarly, we know of no human society that does not have rules about the relationship of the sexes to each other and about the relationship of parents to children. We know of no human society today that does not say it is wrong to kill within some circle; nor do we know of any human society that does not protect in some way the integrity of each individual.

There is a tendency for us to hope that we have reached irreversible stages of knowledge or goodness or power. Yet, in light of what we know of human history, there is no guarantee that any people with any culture, with any degree of apparent power and pre-eminence, with any beauty of religious, ethical, and cosmological structure, has attained something that cannot be lost. There is, likewise, no guarantee that any society will ever make a choice that insures its survival. This is another aspect of the human condition—each people, each generation, is charged with the task of eternal vigilance.

It is true that eternal vigilance as the price of freedom is a culturally limited part of our own tradition, but, as we belong to that tradition we have a right to enjoy that ethical maxim. We know that again and again advances have been lost, and we have no assurance that this will not happen in the future. This means that each generation faces the task of conserving what it has and of making certain that no irreversible loss occurs.

One of the reasons we are in such turmoil at the present time is that the chances of loss have gone up astronomically. In the past the people of a certain continent could have died of the plague, while the people of other continents would remain safe; they had no fear of the plague being transmitted to them. In the past there has been war over Asia, but this did not disturb the American Indian who was quietly developing his civilization on this continent, safe from Genghis Khan.

Today there is no safety from any modern Genghis Khan. We run the risk of engulfing the world in any mistake we make. Certainly, our responsibility has been enormously magnified, and it is possible to think that the power that modern technology has given us is comparable to a second loss of innocence. Man's original capacity to choose, which made him responsible for his own fate to a limited degree, now makes us responsible for the fate not only of some small group, a nation or even an empire, but of the whole of mankind. As nearly as we can tell, this is an irreversible, arrived at within our lifetime. Since there is no possibility of our losing the secret of how to destroy the world, ours is now a different sort of responsibility.

The Current Context

Now let us turn from this level of discussion to the question of the turmoil that is facing the United States at present. We find ourselves arguing about every conceivable issue, such as the "new morality," by which most people mean the new *im*morality. (As long as people were being immoral in quiet and respectful ways, nobody was the least bit worried.) At the moment, youth are demanding the approval of the constituted moral authorities in society: their parents, the clergy, the college and school authorities, the employers, and the law. They are insisting that these authorities sanction new kinds of behavior.

This is a very different thing from simply taking the Ford out on a back road after World War I. At that time there was a real shakeup in morality because the adult world gave up chaperoning. A radical change like that was bound to effect changes in morality in the usual sense of the word, that is, immorality. At present, what we are doing is demanding new rules. Young people are rethinking the whole matter of their relationships with each other and with the generation yet unborn.

We are witnessing a tremendous upheaval in the relationships between the young immature—who are now the majority—and the rest of society. But the youth are not all going one way. While they are fighting for the right to take part in planning college curriculums, and are protesting against a draft in which they do not believe and against a war of which they do not approve, they are not fighting for the eighteen-year-old vote. I think this is one of the most striking things about the present situation. It points up the fact that young people are not only demanding new participation, but also refusing new participation.

This is one reason some of them see nothing to do but walk out, and others see nothing in this country worth saving. They are drastically confused between wanting to play a bigger role and feeling unready to do so. It's a great deal of fun to go to New Hampshire and work for McCarthy, but if anybody started counting and really figured out how much easier it would be to find ten like-minded members of his own age group than to convert all those stubborn New Hampshire farmers, he would realize that the eighteen-year-old vote would get the job done much faster. But youth are not asking for the right to vote. In a recent publication of one of the journals devoted to the nudist movement, we are told that the teenagers in that movement too are rebelling: they wear clothes, on the ground that they have not been given a sufficiently responsible voice in the management of the nudist movement.

I think we have to realize the dichotomy between the shift in responsibility and the age of possible participation. We lower the age of marriage, while raising the age of professional competence. We lower the age at which youth are given terrific responsibilities in war, while at the same time giving them no voice in choosing the war. We lower the age of taxation to the extent that we lower the age of earning. Meanwhile the age of puberty is dropping four months a decade. Children mature earlier and earlier. We are losing the period that Freudians refer to as latency, and others as childhood: between the time you start to school and the time your glands get in the way.

In the second place, the world has never before faced a situation such as we face today in which the mass of the world's people, regardless of their education, or their background, or their religion, or their understanding of any of the issues, are exposed to the same situations. Television is a medium that we do not yet understand. The intellectual and moral leaders of the country have failed to take advantage of it. We need to know how we are going to use this medium which has so drastically changed the relationships of people in the world to each other and to the past and future.

The question of heart transplants has gone all the way around the globe. The whole world heard what was said by the woman whose husband received a new heart. The whole world listened as she was asked whether she thought race was a significant issue or not. Never before have we had such an extensive audience of such disparate backgrounds listening to the same words.

We have also never had a medium that could take daydreaming about the future and treat it as if it were the present. Today we have people with extraordinarily different accesses to the past, and most with no access at all. Access to the past depends either on living in the same community all of your life and at least knowing what your great-uncle did, or on really being able to read. A very limited part of the world really reads, and nobody lives any more where his great-uncle lived if he can help it.

Television attempts to dramatize the digging up of ancient archeological remains and everybody says that the events portrayed happened just yesterday because that is when they were presented to them. I am reminded of what an old woman in Wales said to the Greek archeologist when he dug up a Roman coin: "Do you know what that Julius Caesar did? He had every man in the village out working on the roads." This is approximately our notion of the past: It may be four generations ago or a million years ago and we haven't a clue to the difference.

If we consider the tremendous differences in background and understanding on the part of people throughout the world experiencing simultaneously and vividly through television visions of the past that are not placed and visions of the future that are not placed, and if at the same time we contrast the children born after Sputnik with young people born after the Bomb—two groups growing up in their different ages and trying to understand them—I think we have some explanation for the turmoil we are in. But this does not necessarily mean that the world is coming to an end; it is not a proof that civilization is rotten, the family finished, and marriage dead.

The Conference Issues

Some of the topics of this conference involve predictions, like the one made recently in the *New York Times* to the effect that because we are going to be able to produce human life in some extrauterine fashion—what he called the test tube—the family is going to disappear. Now, the family was here long before anybody knew anything about paternity, and the chances are pretty good that it will survive our finding out some more things. People have bred perfectly beautiful families even where the titular father of the baby has been dead for twelve years; his absence has not interfered at all with family life. I worked with people in New Guinea who had no idea of the length of human gestation. Nobody gets worried there if a woman's husband has been working away from home for a long period and three months after he comes home she has a baby. They just say the baby hurried up to see its father.

There may well be manifold possibilities of creation in the future. We should begin thinking about these possibilities of tampering with the environment, and of tampering with human life, long before they happen instead of long afterwards. A member of the press corps asked me if this conference were not ten years too late, to which I said, "I hope so, because anything that isn't ten years too late would not have a chance of a hearing."

We are confronted with a large number of totally artificial choices. Choices made by individuals who are worried about their hearts are not very valuable. Choices made by people who care about medical ethics may be extremely valuable.

Now, the press is absolutely convinced that there are only two topics before this meeting: one is abortion and the other is heart transplants. I have a great deal of respect for the press, but I would like to widen the context and put these two issues slated for separate discussion into somewhat the same perspective. I should like to take abortion first and place it in cultural perspective.

Abortion

One of the things we have to recognize is that throughout all of human history almost every human group, with a few rather striking exceptions, has been afraid that it would die out. It was therefore deemed necessary for the group to devise social means for its own protection and perpetuation. Sometimes this meant letting girl babies die so that the requisite energy would be put into having and preserving enough boys. Sometimes it meant polygamy, sometimes polyandry. Sometimes it meant an insistence on migration. Sometimes it has led to a great variety of rules. There have been a few times in history when people realized there were too many people in a given small area, but those times were exceptions. As a rule, every human group that we know anything about has been vitally concerned to assure adequate reproduction. The time in which we live is the first time in human history that the survival of the human race depended on reducing the number of children instead of increasing it. It is also the first time in human history that every human group has had to face the fact that if it has too many children it will not be able to care for them the way children need to be cared for today. It is the first time in human history that we are totally dependent on the quality of care, nutrition, and education rather than on sheer numbers.

This new fact has changed the state of the world. It has changed our attitude toward contraception, and it is changing our attitude toward abortion. I think that one should place abortion first within this context, that we are free today at least to discuss the possibility of not giving birth this week to every little human soul beating against the windows of life. For the first time we are asking for some postponement, and this raises a variety of very important issues.

For people who believe in reincarnation—which is a very large part of the world—it raises one kind of issue. But for people who believe that one has only a single life, and the longer one lives it and the longer one keeps one's teeth the better, it raises a different issue; it favors an ethic that is always thinking about the living rather than the unborn.

For those on the other hand who believe in the protection of every human life and locate that human life in conception, the issue is again a different one. One of the things that is happening in some parts of the world is that conception control is now seen as abortion control. That is, adequate contraception makes it possible to do away with abortions. Unless we think in these terms, we lose some of the ethical urgency of this problem.

We are also facing the fact that in this country it has always been customary to try to legislate morality for other people. From the very start we have made laws to interfere with other people's private lives. There was, for example, the rule that you should not kiss your wife on Sunday. We insisted that wherever there was a Protestant majority that did not believe in drinking, everybody else could jolly well stop drinking.

Through the centuries we have seen an erosion both of law and of moral authority every time this happens, Prohibition of course being the outstanding example. Nothing did more to destroy the moral authority of the American middle class than Prohibition. Up to that point parents could pretend they were good when they weren't—which is absolutely essential if you are going to bring up good children—but Prohibition robbed the average liberal parent of this pretense. It was absolutely impossible for him to prove his obedience to the law, and once his obedience became dubious many other things followed. Thus Prohibition was one of the great contributors to the loss of moral authority. Parents began to say, "I don't know what to do . . . it depends on the situation"—and we developed situation ethics.

In the area of race relations, in the matter of alcohol, in all sorts of questions about the division of income and the separation of peoples—in innumerable ways we are forcing on a minority (different minorities, but all minorities) things that they believe are wrong. So what we are getting is an increased realization of the nonviability of laws which in the name of one group's code of ethics force another group of people to do what they believe to be wrong.

I think abortion is an outstanding example of this. First, we passed laws against abortion which served both the interest of society—at a time when we were afraid we did not have enough children—and the interest of religious groups who believed abortion was wrong. Now, another group, believing these abortion laws to be wrong, wants to pass other abortion laws which will violate the ethics of the first group. I believe that one of the things we are going to have to face is that it is wrong—wrong, you understand, in light of the present situation in the country we live in and the period we live in—to legislate in areas of ethical heterogeneity. It is wrong to force any group of people to endorse or abide by laws which they believe to be wrong.

The simplest way of dealing with this is to repeal all abortion laws. Do not have laws. We do not have to have laws regarding abortion at all. The medical profession is perfectly capable of licensing surgeons and keeping them in order. Catholic hospitals can protect Catholics' consciences, and Protestant hospitals can protect Protestants' consciences. To ask Roman Catholics, who believe that the taking of any human life is wrong, to respect or pass or endorse a law approving such an act, is to ask them to behave unethically. On the other hand, to pass a law restricting the action of Protestants and humanitarians who believe differently in this matter is also to ask them to behave unethically.

Similarly, to draft young men who had no chance to vote on or choose to fight in a war that they believe is wrong, at a time when we do not actually need all our young men to fight and our own country is not actually in danger, I think is wrong. It is the same kind of issue. It is an issue on which the country is divided, and the nation should not use its legal strength to coerce people into doing things which, in terms of their own ethics, they believe to be wrong.

It is not a crisis between good and evil, between law and disorder. It is a crisis between different people who have different views of the good, and if we recognize that our young people want the door left open all night or only closed with a piece of paper in it—or any of these other arguments that are going on—then we will recognize that what they are asking for is parental review and change of the old rules which they feel are no longer viable.

Heart Transplants

The heart transplant is far more complicated. It is primarily a question of whether or not we are going to keep the kind of medical profession we have attained with such an enormous ethical advance over the long course of human history. When the Hippocratic oath was invented the medical profession said: From now on we are faithful only to life, and under no circumstances will we ever be involved in taking a life, no matter how old or how young or how evil that life may be, whether it be the life of a robber or the life of the governor, or even of the head of state, whether individually rich or poor, male or female, black or white or yellow; no matter who they are or what they are, we will help them live. The medical profession has just one obligation, and that is to keep life alive.

Most of us do not realize the importance of this stance as keenly as we might. I am acutely aware of it, having lived in societies in which killer and curer is the same person. Perhaps you have been in one of these situations where you are angry at the doctor because he did not give your mother some pills so she could commit suicide. Perhaps you have known someone who gave birth to a deformed baby and feels that the doctor should have killed that baby at birth, or at least not let it live. Unless you have been in such a situation, where you yourself have wanted to tempt the physician into the position of killing, it is hard to realize what the Hippocratic obligation has meant to the human race, and to the whole of medicine as we know it today. All the advances that have been made in the field of medicine are due to this one, simple, great invention.

The average human being does not like this extraordinary invention very well because there are lots of situations when he would prefer to get the doctor to intervene on the side of death rather than life. We do not want hopelessly deformed children to live. We do not want hapless old people kept alive like human vegetables by intravenous feeding for months and months, while the family watches its entire resources dwindle away, knowing that the old folks themselves, had they been conscious, would have hated it. There are dozens of things we do not want to happen, and it is always a temptation to say that the doctor should prevent them.

It is really up to the body politic to protect this priceless invention which made the medical profession absolutely faithful to life. There will be no help from the medical people themselves in this regard, for they are pledged to life. Besides, the fact that they deal with life makes them sometimes a little omnipotent. People sometimes say that decision in these critical matters is up to the doctor, and that old people should have the right to decide that they do not want to live, at least not to live in a helpless and meaningless way. But then the doctor must ask, "All right, who is going to tell them?"

Thus, in the end the whole tendency is always to drop the question into the lap of the medical profession. But we cannot count on the medical profession alone not to disavow its commitment. We must therefore protect them in spite of themselves.

This heart transplant argument, as nearly as I can see, has three prongs. One is the argument that if two people need a heart, which one is going to get it? But this hasn't a thing to do with hearts; it is true about food and antibiotics. If you haven't enough vaccine to vaccinate everybody you go to work and get more. So this is not really the question. We have an insufficiency of most things in the world, but we don't say, "Therefore, you should not have any vaccine because there is not enough for the other person as well."

Then you hear people argue that the transplant operation is hazardous, and here I think the medical profession is fully on its rights in saying that all advances in surgery come from taking risks. One of the things we ask of a physician, and one of the things for which we reward him with our respect and reverence, is his willingness to take risks. The patient too has a right to take a risk, and the physician has a right to decide that, if the patient is willing, he will take the risk with him.

The real issue that we are talking about—and attempting to dodge by bringing in these other questions—is the issue of whether the physician should ever be asked to perform, on a patient who still has any life left in him at all, an operation which means certain death. This is the issue we are worried about and this is the issue we have yet to answer. And herein lies the drama of the present moment, for up to this point in history the physician has always stood on the side of the patient to his last quivering breath. We have even seen times when people we thought to be dead were not dead, and people who on good medical authority were thought to be doomed to die did not die. The church has even allowed for the administration of extreme unction up to, I think, twenty-four hours after "death." You cannot tell when someone is actually dead. Simply to recognize this fact is a notable advance over a situation in New Guinea, where the people are quite certain when someone has died: Even though he may still be breathing they say he just doesn't know himself.

Any request for action to save life by taking life means that the more faithful we are to life, the more we must protect the medical

profession from ever being asked to take it. If we want a society in which older people, acting with the dignity of an Eskimo grandmother, decide they will no longer be a burden on the young, then that must be the decision of individual human beings, not of their doctors. Society itself must back up such individual decisions instead of trying to force it on the profession that has devoted itself entirely to life.

These are the sorts of issues that change with each generation, sometimes within weeks or months. And because of TV, and because something may happen anywhere in the world, tomorrow morning we may be faced with the ethics of Buddhists or Moslems or Christians who have taken on the burdens of their own native culture instead of that of Western Christianity. We are faced every day with an array of confusion that we never had before, but we should not confuse the confusion with destruction or deterioration. What we need to do is to learn how to deal with the confusion in the terms in which it has arisen.

* * *

DR. NORBECK: Dr. Mead, in discussing what she has aptly called the new immorality, has given us an interesting and, I would say, very clear picture of something we refuse to believe. That is, that morals, conceptions of morals, are relative; they change with time and place. But we know better—people of my age at least. We learned the moral standards a long time ago, and are most reluctant to give them up.

I have been working on just this issue in Japan. If it is any comfort to you, the circumstances in Japan are precisely what they are here. A large part of the nation—the people in their forties and up—is decrying the loss of morals. Now that nation is not a land of moral chaos or anarchy any more than this nation is.

There are problems. This was all expressed very well quite a long time ago. It was expressed, as a matter of fact, in poetry.

> There is no good; there is no bad;
> These be the whims of mortal man.
> What works me well, that I call good;
> What harms me or hurts I hold as bad.
> They change with time; they change with place;

And in the various span of time
What's bad has won a fortune's crown.
What's good is banned as sin or crime.[2]

This is Sir Richard Burton a long time ago. None of us ever believed it.

We have done some strange things in keeping with our technology, and I want to ask Dr. Mead a question in that context. What we have done has pushed up the age of maturity. It is a very good thing that we do not have puberty rites or coming of age ceremonies because we would not know when to hold them. At what age one comes of age in our society is a great mystery today. We have the immature at age thirty. Many on this campus are immature by our reckoning because they are still being educated. On the other hand, we pushed the other end of the span of life way up. If we were dealing with people as we do with the praying mantis or parrot, we would divide the life span into three parts: youth—ages one to twenty-five, middle age—twenty-five to fifty, and old age—fifty to seventy-five. This means that a large part of our immature students on this campus are well into middle age. The nation is very much a gerontocracy if we come to points.

We find that the conceptions of morality are changing mainly among the young. That fits our social-cultural scene. On the other hand, a very large number of our people are middle-aged and older. We know also that as we age we become less and less elastic. We want to hang on to the standards of time gone by. Now, I shall ask Dr. Mead how she thinks this will all be resolved, how it might be resolved, or if it is being resolved right now.

DR. MEAD: I don't agree, you know, that as people get older they get more inflexible. The thing that makes people flexible is the experience of successful change. If they go to other countries and eat other foods and sleep in other kinds of beds and learn other kinds of languages, then we call them flexible, sophisticated, cosmopolitan.

I ask you, Dr. Norbeck: Who has experienced more successful change in this country—the twenty-year-olds or the eighty-year-olds? Eighty-year-olds today have traversed the greatest and most rapid change the world has ever known, and if they think there is something on the television screen, if they use the telephone without

[2] Sir Richard Francis Burton, ed. and trans., *The Kasidah of Haji Abdu el-Yezdi* (Philadelphia: David McKay Co., 1931), bk. 5, p. 43.

shouting, if they still drive a car that did not exist when they were children, if they can learn the names of the new African nations and deal with the center of Asia, if they can understand what a guaranteed annual income is, then, I submit they have crossed more boundaries more successfully and learned to live with more funny kinds of things and more strange people they never dreamed of meeting than have the young.

What we need to do is to change this idea that the old are rigid. We need to invent institutions that will give to older people, who have traveled and eaten something besides eggs and bacon and have experienced much change, an opportunity to teach the very young what change is all about. In other words, Dr. Norbeck, what we need to do is to invent those institutions which can incorporate change into the educational system. Unless we do that, we are stuck. By demoting people too early, by spreading the notion that when they reach a given age they are hopeless, cannot learn, and are not useful in any way, we have created a great mass of hopeless, despairing, laid-on-the-shelf people in this country. Then, we aid another social science myth that says that older people want to be disengaged.

Researchers have failed to find such people when they really look. There are very few who want to be disengaged, unless they are great-great-grandparents and saints. The rest of the country clearly wants to be engaged, and if we can invent ways of engaging them, this will feed back into the experience of little children the successful confrontation of change by their elders.

We can teach the young people today who are worried about the Bomb and what it means. They just do not know about the Bomb and what it means because they do not know. They are afraid they will be blown up, because that is all they are being taught. They are not being taught of the change that took place in man's whole responsibility to the world when the Bomb came; they are not being told that now for the first time we really have a chance to prevent war. They are just being taught something that is perfectly contemporary and does not include the past. So that, I think, is my principal answer to your principal challenge.

I did not like that poem either, because it suggests that there is no difference between good and bad. I believe, all we know at the present about human evolution suggests that man's capacity to choose, to say that one course is right and another wrong, is an essential aspect of human nature and of human nature's participation in the evolutionary process.

This does not mean that one has to phrase it in religious terms. One could phrase it in simple biological terms. The content varies, but the essential belief that certain things are right and certain things are wrong—and the capacity to be taught this distinction and to teach it—are, I believe, in the light of what we know at present about human evolution, something that we can regard as intrinsic in the human race. You know, whenever we have a rebellion in this country the kids send in the question, "Ought one to have a conscience?"

DR. EVANS: I would like to state, first of all, a very sharp disagreement with Dr. Norbeck's observation that he felt that Dr. Mead was presenting to us a new immorality that is evidenced by all these developments. I could not disagree more. I think that in her work and her approach to things, I always see something that is very crucial. Let me elaborate just a bit.

There has been an age-long problem in the history of theology and the history of physiology which we are just beginning to take seriously in the field of social psychology. This is the dimension: "hope—despair." This problem has been dealt with in every conceivable way, certainly, but most powerfully I think in an area where empirical behavioral science can join with somewhat more abstract theological reasoning, and that is the area surrounding and dealing with what is called "self-fulfilling prophecy."

Essentially what we mean by this is that if you believe something is going to happen, the very nature of that belief will increase the probability of its happening. One illustration I think is very apropos at the moment. If we keep talking about long, hot summers, and over and over again express our belief in their recurrence, this may contribute immeasurably to the possibility that long, hot summers will indeed occur. For example, I hold the media to be responsible for balancing their presentations in such a way that rumors of such possible eventualities will not be confused with good, basic, sound information that may help us to protect society.

I believe that in the message of people in our culture like Dr. Mead we have consistently a message of hope. To illustrate what I mean, let us take her observations on student protests.

Some of us who look at this problem empirically recognize some rather important variables in such student protests as those in the United States at the moment, and the kind of existentialist protests which we saw in France fifteen or twenty years ago. At that particular time I happened to be in France. I spoke with a number of students and was very taken with the destructive despair that characterized them. They were not organizing necessarily to change something. They saw something they thought their protests would remedy. And when it did not, in many instances an almost apathetic despair set in, so that out of this "existentialist" group—I am putting the term in quotation marks because it has so many different connotations—I felt that little of significance happened in France. All we really got out of it was, perhaps, a generation of reconsideration of existentialism, but not anything very important as far as a hope of change is concerned.

By contrast, look at just the preliminary information that we now have on the student protest movement in the United States. I think if we talked to these students—at least this is my feeling as regards my campus—there is much hope. They have some great belief that what they are doing can change things.

And I quite agree with Dr. Mead that the McCarthy campaign is a very excellent example of how something unlike the French student protest group can develop into something that is very constructive. I think there is no question that the phenomenon of the McCarthy movement is a direct spinoff of student protest. I suspect the reason that Dr. Mead raised this question of the student protest movement is that we might argue that out of the behavior of our young people really come the foundations for the ethics that will be so crucial in this era of powerful changes in technology and in the biological sciences. To argue that the activity and vitality of our young people seems to be directed toward the hope that something can indeed be changed, goes very well for an ethic, because probably the most important ethic of all is faith, faith that we can better the life of mankind. This is quite consistent with most of the outgoing behavior patterns of our students at the moment. Whether we handle these behavior patterns appropriately and see them in an optimistic way or as a threat to institutions is another matter.

I would like also to underline a point that Dr. Mead made about the relationship between aging and receptivity to innovation.

In our recent study of ten American universities, which focused particularly on university professors,[3] we tried to look both at professors who were innovators, who wanted to move forward in change, and at professors who were more resistant to change. It is interesting that, far from what we predicted, very often age was not a factor at all. In fact, it was more likely that the older professors were moving in the direction of innovation while the younger ones were frightened, anxious, and insecure, afraid to change.

The system is responsible for this to some degree. I hope you understand that I am not necessarily blaming the young professors, but their stance is not exactly what you might have expected on the basis of these sometimes naive generalizations to the effect that age necessarily leads to greater rigidity. I gather that what is involved in such a generalization, at least in part, is this matter of the self-fulfilling prophecy; If you think that because you are getting old you have to become more detached and resistant to change, you probably will. We have a lot of evidence already of people continuing to function well in their status role in a hierarchy after the age of sixty-five, or even after seventy. This is a very interesting area for study. We have found indeed that it is not necessary that older people withdraw.

One of the points that is of great concern to me, reflecting a point that Dr. Mead made, was the responsibility for decision-making on the part of the innovator in science. Let me give a concrete example. Dr. Christian Barnard appeared before a subcommittee of the United States Senate that was exploring the very issues that are at stake in this conference. His testimony is at once shocking and interesting. He made the statement that to set various types of laws and regulations, whether within medicine or outside of medicine, in an attempt to control the physician was kind of ridiculous because, he felt, in the final analysis every physician worth his salt would already have at his command the capability for ethical choice.

Now, this is a bit disturbing, though at the same time you might say, "Well, maybe he is projecting, maybe he himself feels that he has this great capacity for ethical choice." But it further indicates that in our culture very often a person who may be ill equipped to

[3] See Richard I. Evans and P. K. Leppman, *Resistance to Innovation in Higher Education* (San Francisco: Jossey-Bass, 1968).

deal with more complicated human problems, if he becomes an innovator, suddenly establishes considerable credibility for himself as a judge of the human problem, the decision-making situation.

Since Dr. Norbeck raised a question for Dr. Mead, I too would like to challenge her. Since so many people enter a conference such as this merely to protect their own existing points of view, and are not necessarily interested in contributing to a new dialogue, is there any hope that such a conference can have some impact beyond that?

DR. MEAD: I want to deal first with this question of new morality or immorality. What I had said was that when we talk about the new morality, most people think in terms of what they call immorality. Many think that the new morality means you have lost the old morality, and if you have lost the old morality, you are naturally immoral.

I did not say I believed in that.

We talk as if when we say new morality, most people mean immorality. But this is not what the kids mean. What the kids mean is that some of the old rules that don't fit the contemporary situations ought to be changed. "We don't think that what you are asking of us is consonant with what you are permitting us and, stated quite bluntly, a society that continues to preach premarital chastity and reward premarital pregnancy doesn't make any sense."

This is what we do today. "College authorities, clergy, parents —they all reward you the minute you are pregnant: you can have anything you like." But, of course, we all believe in premarital chastity and I have no idea how we believe people get pregnant.

This turned up when I proposed that we have a two years' waiting period before people could be declared to be suitable for becoming parents and giving life to children. People said of the proposal, "But how would you keep them from getting pregnant?" And I said, "The way a lot of people manage now." They somehow thought that marriage made you pregnant. So I really don't think that Dr. Norbeck said I thought this was new immorality.

Now, this self-fulfilling prophecy point is, I think, much more complicated than first meets the eye, and we have to watch out what we make of it. The riot situation is, of course, most acute at the moment; it affects everybody in the whole country.

In the middle of World War II after the second bad riot—those of you old enough to remember will recall that we had only two riots in World War II, one in Detroit and one in Birmingham—a meeting was called in Chicago of persons throughout the country, black and white, who were profoundly interested in race relations and were believed to have some competence in leadership. At that meeting the self-fulfilling prophecy people said, "We can talk about the danger of riots and we will have them. Men who carry guns always in the end shoot somebody." Here we have a heavy dose of the self-fulfilling prophecy. We overruled those people and said, "There is danger in this country and we must meet it." And every city developed a committee of people who did not want riots, and we did not have riots. In spite of everything that everybody prophesied about the terrible things that were going to happen when the Negro troops who had been in France came home, we did not have a race riot until 1951—and then it was a furniture riot. As you may remember, in Cicero, Illinois, there was an attempt at integrating a housing project. A Negro moved his family in, and all the people who wanted to riot came over and threw his furniture out and threw everybody else's furniture out. But we did not have any race riots, not because people were not afraid, but because they were effectively organized to prevent something they did not want to happen.

The trouble at present is that there are a great number of people in this country who want riots, and they are not all found on the left—or on the right or in the middle. There are simply vested interests of every sort. To begin with, the press and other media set up cameras and they don't want things interfered with before they get a good picture. And this has happened right around the world. There are people who think we are too slow. There are the kids who do not have the vote and are not willing to take the vote. There are the masses of people who want riots, and there are the people who don't want them but haven't come forward and haven't acted, so it is a self-fulfilling prophecy to just sit around and predict that it is going to be a long, hot summer and we are going to have riots. But I don't think we can simply say that by pointing out the danger, we thereby increase it. If we say there is a danger and then do nothing about it, or are content to let the army deal with it, then we will indeed have trouble.

I would like to use as an illustration of this whole point about self-fulfilling propositions the era of Joseph McCarthy. There were a fair number of us then who, knowing American history, didn't think the McCarthy era would mark the end of the world, or that our country would turn into a fascist state and everyone would be sent to a concentration camp. But if we had said so, and said it in such a way as sufficiently to convince all the people who at the time were trying to defeat McCarthy and liberalize the behavior of the House Un-American Activities Committee, McCarthy would have won.

This is a trap in America that I think we have to look at, and that is related to this conference. We are facing a crisis, and nobody would listen if we were not facing a crisis. We have to deal with the truth of our own culture, and if our own culture depends on viewing everything with alarm, then the people all go home the way they did in the 1950's.

A conference like this has the task of saying two things at once. On the one hand, the situation is very grave. That must be said. It is very late, and if we do not control the things that are happening in this world, if we let technology run wild, we will destroy our atmosphere, land, water, and sea; the population explosion will completely engulf us, and we will blow ourselves up with nuclear weapons. At one level this is true, and we have to say it. But we have also to say that there are some things that can be done in the light of this danger, and that if we take cognizance of the danger in time to act, something will happen.

Now, I suppose that Dr. Evans is really making remarks about faculty and inter-disciplinary rivalries and things like that, and the fear that this conference will do what so many conferences like it have done—break down over professional disputes and get nowhere. I would hope that this need not happen. I would hope that, in the tradition that Rice imposes, the issues are important enough to transcend such academic rivalries, and that the age range of the participants is wide enough to include the depth and breadth of our present dilemmas and our present possibilities.

2. Technology and Values

One of the most stimulating sessions of the conference centered on the address of Dr. Emmanuel Mesthene concerning value formation. Here were raised many of the great overriding social-ethical issues which underlay the various specific concerns of the conference. What, asked Dr. Mesthene, are the factors that contribute to the shaping of the values that are operative? How are technology and religion related to values? He dealt with the formative power of technology and of religion as well as with the creative intersection of the two. The session involved a rare blending of philosophic depth with the consideration of hard reality.

Both philosopher and social scientist, Dr. Mesthene has served as a special consultant to the President of the United States on science and technology. His writing in the field of technology and values has had wide interdisciplinary significance. He is presently director of the Program on Technology and Society at Harvard University.

The several reactors brought scintillating responses from their various perspectives. Dr. Margaret Mead and Dr. Richard Evans enriched the discussion, as did Dr. Charles Jones, president of Humble Oil Company. In addition, there were several stimulating questions from the audience.

Technology and Values

Emmanuel G. Mesthene

Definition of Terms

As a devoted follower of Socrates, I might appropriately begin by defining the terms of my title. I understand by "technology" the totality of the tools that men make and use to make and do things with. The technology of a time or society, then, is its tool-box, which I construe broadly to include, not only hand tools and machines, but also the spectrum of intellectual tools, from language, to ideas, to science, and to such latterday techniques as computer programs, systems analysis, and program planning and budgeting systems.

The concept of technology in this way begins to shade into the broader concept of knowledge. There are a number of important issues, in fact, that may have little connection with technology as such, but that are nevertheless relevant to technology by virtue of illuminating the social role of knowledge in general—construing knowledge, in this general sense, to include information, intellectual methodology, a commitment to rationality, and the host of knowledge institutions from universities, to research and development institutes, to analysis and planning staffs in public and private organizations.

In other words, it is through enhancing the status, office, and importance of knowledge in one or another of its forms that science and technology may affect society most significantly. In that sense, understanding technology in the broader sense of knowledge—in the ancient sense of *scientia,* if you will—may be a precondition of understanding the effects of technology on values, or on society generally.

The other term in my title is "values," and definition here is more difficult. It is often customary to distinguish rather sharply between individual and social values and, in another dimension, between preferences on the one hand (which are usually thought of as short-term, low-level, and localized), and values on the other hand (which are seen as high-level, relatively long-term, and extensive in scope). A taste for automobile fins is thus generally accounted a preference, whereas a taste for freedom is called a value.

This distinction is useful for a number of scientific and practical purposes, but I think it has no standing in logic. I agree, on this point, with the noted economist, Kenneth Arrow: "One may want to reserve the term 'values' for a specially elevated or noble set of choices. Perhaps choices in general might be referred to as 'tastes.' We do not ordinarily think of the preference for additional bread over additional beer as being a value worthy of philosophic inquiry.

I believe, though, that the distinction cannot be made logically. . . ."[1] The *logical* equivalence of preferences and values, whether individual or social, derives from the fact that all are rooted in the choice behavior of human beings. For contemporary American sociology, for example, values are broad, dominant, and extensive commitments that account for the cohesion of society and for the maintenance of its identity through time. Values in this sense are related to choice both in their genesis (i.e., as abstractions from choice patterns typical of a particular society) and in their exemplification (i.e., as criteria of further choice-making).

It is with values in this sense that I will be principally concerned here, although I want to attend also to the kinds of values that we call religious. I shall be concentrating on the nature of the relationship between technology and values, that is, on some of the mechanisms, the ways, by which technological change leads to value change. I will allude to value changes actually discernible in present-day society only by way of illustration, without discussing them in detail.

Does Technology Threaten Values?

One way to approach an understanding of the technology/values relationship is by examining the considerable concern expressed in many quarters these days that technological advances may so affect the fabric of the whole society as to pose a threat to our values and ideals. Some writers—Jacques Ellul, Arthur Koestler, Lewis Mumford, and Joseph Wood Krutch, for example—go so far as to assert a fundamental incompatibility between technology and values and to warn that technological progress is tantamount to dehumanization and to destruction of all value. There are grains of truth covered over with tons of confusion in such writings, in my opinion, and it is important to discover where the one ends and the other begins.

There is no question that some values are destroyed in the process of technological change. Traditional values attaching to a rural and craft-based economy are destroyed by industrialization

[1] Kenneth J. Arrow, "Public and Private Values," in Sidney Hook, ed., *Human Values and Economic Policy* (New York: New York University Press, 1967), p. 4.

and urbanization, and the values we associate with individual privacy and individual enterprise are weakened as social policies and decisions become increasingly technical, long range, information based, expert dominated, and machine processed. Other values take the place of those that are lost, of course, but frequently at the cost of punishing traumata of adjustment for particular individuals and particular groups that it would be immoral to ignore.

Further, there are positive disvalues implicit in some technologies (as in environmental pollution or the death and maiming that sometimes attend the introduction of new drugs or vaccines) as well as callous disregard of the values of others (as when political and industrial interests engaged in developing a new technology have the vested interest and powerful means to urge its adoption and widespread use irrespective of social utility). The destruction of value is justly inveighed against in such cases and warrants all the political vigilance we can muster.

On the other hand, I find no justification for the contention that technological progress must *of necessity* mean a progressive destruction of value. The fear that it does is based partly on psychological resistance to change and partly, I think, on a currently fashionable literary conceit that sees a loss of value in the fact that the average man today does not share the values characteristic of small aristocratic elites of centuries ago, when most men lived like brutes, submerged from observation. Beyond that, I think the fear that technology is by nature threatening to values has its source, partly in an event in the history of science, but mainly in a fundamental misunderstanding of the nature of value.

Modern science—and especially modern physics, which serves as an ideal model for science—characteristically avoids explanations in terms of purpose. Ancient and medieval science, by contrast, postulated four "causes"—four principles of explanation—of any process, of which the most important was the final cause, that is, the purpose for which a process could be said to occur. If we now recall that meanings and values can exist only in relation to processes or behaviors that can be understood as purposeful, we see a basic logical compatibility between values and the ancient concept of science, provided that not only knowledge as such but also the understanding necessary to the achievement of human purposes is recognized. Science thus contributed to the generation and preservation of value. The idea that science might threaten value could not but be alien and contradictory in such a view.

The danger in this approach, of course, was that the scientific search for truth could be distorted by politically or religiously motivated substitution of purposes antithetical to the logic of inquiry. Just that began to happen in medieval times, with the result that purpose was converted from an explanatory concept that aided understanding to an externally imposed constraint that interfered with it. In response, modern science simply abandoned purpose as a principle of intellectual organization. This was made easier, of course, by the fact that modern science flourished first in the fields of astronomy and mathematical physics, in which purpose had in fact no scientific value. (It had been a purely formal concept even in ancient astronomy, since the movement of the heavenly bodies was seen as eternal and therefore not a process in time requiring explanation in terms of the end toward which the process could be seen to be tending.)

What had thus seemed to the ancients a natural compatibility between science and value (which they termed the unity of knowledge and virtue) was upset by the abandonment by science of the concept of end or purpose. Causation was thenceforth limited to efficiency, that is, to the "pushing-from-behind" or motive factor that served to *initiate* a process, like putting a ball in motion by pushing it. This made scientific explanation mechanical and wholly independent of meaning, and therefore independent, too, of all considerations of value. Then followed the long and dismal history of the science/value dualism, whose contemporary form is the assertion of an antinomy between technology and human values.

There is nothing in that history, however, to justify the inference that is too often made from it that the idea of end or purpose and the ideas of science and technology are antithetical by nature. Indeed, the science of biology has continued to make use of teleological explanation—that is, explanation in terms of ends—even after its transition into the modern period. Nor can the social sciences eschew teleological explanation if they are to go beyond description in terms of accepted categories to genuine understanding of the human (and therefore purposeful) processes that they inquire into. Even physics, for that matter, whose subject matter it is certainly nonsense to think of as purposeful or value-laden, cannot itself, as a human enterprise, be wholly free of human purposes. The noted sociologist of science, Robert Merton, has noted, for example, what he calls "the demonstrable fact that the thematics of science in 17th-century England were in large part determined by the social structure of the time."[2] As we, in our century, make increasingly deliberate use of our science and technology in pursuit of our social purposes, I think that the technology/values dualism, which began as a historical accident, will be completely overcome in time.

The principal source of the view that technology and values are incompatible by nature is, I believe, a confusion of what is valuable with what is stable. The values of a society change more slowly, to be sure, than do the realities of human experience; their persistence is inherent in their emergence as values in the first place and in their function as criteria, which means that their own adequacy will tend to be judged later rather than earlier. But values do change, as a glance at any history will show. They do not have to be eternal and unchanging in order to be values.

Moreover, values change more quickly the more quickly society itself changes as a result of rapid technological advance. Since technological change is so prominent a characteristic of our own society, we tend to note inadequacies in our received values more quickly than might have been the case in other times. When that perception is coupled with the conviction I have been criticizing, that technology and value are inherently inimical to each other, the opinion is strengthened that technological advance must mean the decline of values and of the amenities of distinctively human civilization.

While particular values may vary with particular times and particular societies, however, the human activity of valuing and the social function of values do not change. That is the source of the stability necessary to moral experience. This will not be found, nor should it be sought, exclusively in the familiar values of the past. As the world and society are seen increasingly as processes in constant change under the impact of new technology, value analysis will have to concentrate on process too: on the process of valuation

[2] Robert K. Merton, *Social Theory and Social Structure* (Glencoe, Ill.: The Free Press, 1949), p. 348.

in the individual and on the process of value formation and value change in society. The emphasis will have to shift, in other words, from values, as stable, known, and familiar, to the conditions for and mechanisms of valu*ing*. For it is not existing values as such that are valuable, but the human ability to extract values from experience and to use and cherish them. And *that* value, I would argue, is not threatened by technology; it is only challenged to remain adequate to human experience as that experience is modified under the impact of technological change. I should now like to examine somewhat more closely just how technological change affects the process of valuing and leads to value changes in society.

How Technology Changes Values

Values, in the sociological sense in which I have been discussing them so far, are rather high-level abstractions, so that it is unlikely that technological change can be seen to influence them directly. We need rather, as I suggested earlier, to explore the difference that technology makes for the choice behaviors from which social values are abstracted.

What we can choose is limited, at any given time, by the options available. This is true both of individual choices and of social choices, whether social choices are made deliberately by co-operative public action or whether they are the resultants of a multitude of private choices. (This limitation of choice behavior by the available choice options, incidentally, distinguishes preferences and values, on the one hand, from aspirations and ideals, on the other hand, since aspirations and ideals can attach to imaginative constructs. To confuse the two is to confuse morality and fantasy.)

Now, the first order effect of a new technology is to make possible what was not possible before, and thus to make available new options that were not available before. For example, space technology makes it possible, for the first time, to go to the moon, or to communicate by satellite, and thereby adds these two new options to the spectrum of choices available to the society. By adding new options in this way, technology alters the material conditions of choosing, in just the same way that the sudden appearance of new dishes on the heretofore standard menu of one's favorite restaurant may alter the structure of one's preferences among the older set of menu items. And since values originate in the pattern of antecedent choice behaviors, alteration of the behaviors by alteration of their material conditions can be expected—given appropriate mediating changes and time lags—to lead to alteration of values too.

In short, by making available new options, new technology can lead to a restructuring of the hierarchy of a society's values, either by providing new means for bringing previously unattainable ideals within the realm of choice (i.e., of realizable values), or by altering the relative ease with which different values can be implemented (i.e., by changing the costs associated with realizing them). For example, economic affluence consequent on technological advance may enhance the values we associate with leisure at the relative expense of the values of work and achievement. Or, the advent and use of pain-killing and pleasure-producing drugs can make the value of material comfort relatively easier of achievement than the values we associate with maintaining a stiff upper lip during pain or adversity.

One may argue further that technological change leads to value change, not of any sort at random, but of a particular sort. If this is so, by the way, it provides the ground for some ability, however limited, to forecast the direction of value change in a technological society. The argument for the proposition that technological change leads to value changes of a particular sort centers around the fact that certain attitudes and values are more conducive than others to most effective exploitation of the potentialities of new technologies. Choice behavior has to be somehow attuned to the new options that technology creates if these options are to be chosen. Thus, to transfer or adapt industrial technologies to underdeveloped nations is only part of the solution to the problem of economic development; the more important part consists in altering value predispositions and attitudes so that the technologies can flourish. In more advanced societies, such as ours, people who hold values well adapted to exploitation of major new technologies tend to grow rich and occupy elite positions in society, thus serving to reinforce those same values in the society at large.

Another mechanism that makes for value change upon the introduction of new technology is implicit in the difference between expectation and reality. At any given time, decisions to develop and adopt a new technology will be made according to the values prevailing in society at that time and in the light of the foreseeable consequences of the proposed technology. But since it is of the essence of technology to create new possibilities, there is an irreducible element of uncertainty—of unforeseeable consequence—in any innovation. Techniques of the class of systems analysis are designed to anticipate as much of this uncertainty as possible, but they can never be more than partially successful, partly because a new technology will, in a complex society, enter into interaction with an indefinite number of ongoing processes, and partly—at least in democratic societies—because some of the consequences of technological innovation may take the form of unforeseeable *political* reactions by certain groups in the society.

Since there is an irreducible element of uncertainty that attends every case of technological innovation, therefore, there is need for two evaluations—two acts of judgment: one before and one after the innovation. The first is an evaluation of prospects (of ends-in-view, as John Dewey called them[3]) on the basis of which the choice to develop the technology is made. The second is an evaluation of results (of outcomes actually achieved) which are the actual basis on which future choices will be made. The uncertainty inherent in technological innovation means there will usually be a difference between the conclusions of the two evaluations. To that extent, the material conditions of choice will change, and value changes can be expected to follow.

Values and Religious Myths

An understanding of the implications of technological change —or, better yet, of a technological society—for specifically religious values, requires, I think, a general look at the nature of what men have called God, as well as an analysis of the differences and connections between religious values and social values. I should like to say a few words about each in turn.

I begin with the observation that every human society we know anything about has displayed what can only be described as a religious commitment, however much the content of that commitment may vary from society to society and from age to age. I con-

[3] John Dewey, *Theory of Valuation,* in *International Encyclopedia of Unified Science* (Chicago: University of Chicago, 1939), vol. 2, no. 4.

clude that there is a distinctively religious dimension to human experience which is related to but different from physical, social, psychological, intellectual, or strictly aesthetic experience. I conclude, further, that the *object* of religious experience—the object that satisfies man's specifically religious needs, if you wish—is distinct from the objects involved in other kinds of experience.

The formulation I am employing implies that religious experience involves some sort of object, that is, something objective. I do not mean that this something is objective in the sense of being physical, of course. I mean it is objective in the sense of being a social object, rather than simply the subjective figment of individual imagination. This means that religion is a social experience. If the object of religious experience is a social object, however, its content will be relative to the particular society in which it functions as a religious object. This is consistent with our observation that religious commitments are different in different societies, and it means further that the particular object of religious experience can be expected to change as society changes.

Such a religious relativism violates one's religious sense, however, because, whatever else religious need might be, it is at least a need to identify with something eternal. The answer to this dilemma has been prefigured, I think, in the distinction I drew earlier between specific values of specific societies and the human commitment to value and valuing that provides the stable underpinning of moral experience. I should like to make the analogy explicit.

A social object adequate to religious experience must, I think, have intellectual, moral, aesthetic, and emotional dimensions: it must be consistent with what we know; it must coincide with what we value; it must accord with how we see the world; and it must embody our sense of the unity and therefore the meaningfulness of human experience. But the functioning of the religious object as such is not constrained by what it is specifically that we know, or value, or see, or feel at any given time. It is independent of particular contents—and it is therefore eternal—because what it does, rather, is to help us celebrate and glory in the fact that man can know, and value, and see, and find meaning in his experience. Only man, so far as we know, has this need and capacity to revel in the ideal possibilities implicit in his own nature—what has been called the divine spark in man. And since celebration, glorification, and ritual revelry are social activities above all, men act religiously—that is, share a religious experience—when they join together to worship a common vision of what man might be ideally if he could weaken or sever his earthly bond and transcend himself. That vision of ideal possibility, when clothed in mythological language appropriate to their particular experience, is what men call God.

If we now attend more closely to the moral component of religious experience, we find a similar process of idealization taking place, in which distinctively religious values emerge as a transformation and unification of social values and of ethical values, that is, of those aspects of value that concern the sociologist and the moral philosopher respectively. The sociologist, as I indicated earlier, sees values as definitory of the "temperament" of a society. A society's system of values is the generalized framework of categories according to which the behavior of groups and individuals in that society can be understood. The sociologist is of course investigating what we might call the "ought"-structure of society, but only as an aid to understanding the moral and legal norms that guide action in concrete situations. To that extent, the sociologist's concern with values is descriptive.

The moral philosopher's concern, by contrast, is prescriptive. He is interested in discovering not only what the "ought"-structure of a society or individual is, but what it *should* be. To do this, he not only looks at cultural history and social experience, but also tries to explore the conditions that are imposed on moral action by the nature of man and the nature of nature. He seeks to formulate generalized ideas of good and evil and to use these as criteria for normative judgments of behavior, offering them as guides to moral action.

Both social values and ethical values involve abstraction and generalization. Social values are generalized "conceptions of desirable states of affairs" (as the sociologist Robin Williams has put it[4]) that are abstracted from concrete choice behaviors. Ethical values are, in a similar formula, generalized conceptions of good and evil that are abstracted from the imperatives of specifically moral choices.

[4] Robin M. Williams, Jr., "Individual and Group Values," *Annals of the American Academy of Political and Social Science* 371 (May 1967): 23.

If we now engage in a further abstraction from ethical values at the moral philosopher's level, we arrive at a higher-level generalization of good and evil in some ultimate sense of those terms.

It is at this level and in this sense that values are of interest, in the first instance, to the metaphysician (i.e., to the technical philosopher who investigates the nature of existence as such). But it is also at this level and in this sense that values begin to concern the theologian. I say "begin to," because there remains a difference between the metaphysical and the theological concern with values. The metaphysician deals with ultimate good and evil as abstractions. The theologian is interested also in having the sense of ultimate good and evil infuse actual religious experience. It cannot do that, however, so long as these remain pure abstractions, any more than the idealized vision of human possibility I mentioned a moment ago can function as an object of religious experience so long as it remains only a vision. *Both* must be clothed in the language of myth.

It is in religious myths, then, that both the vision of the divine and the sense of ultimate value take on a form which enables them to function in religious experience. The form, as in all myths, is that of a story, an idealized or imaginative narrative. In its form, therefore, a religious myth is first of all a work of artistic creation—an aesthetic object—which is perfectly appropriate when you recall that religious experience is first of all an experience of celebration and glorification, of enjoyment if you will, of perfectibility and value as ideal possibility. It is no accident that, of the full and varied spectrum of human experience, the religious is most akin to the aesthetic.

It is in religious myths, moreover, that we find also the connection between religious values and social values. For myths, like all stories, can perform their function only if they have artistic credibility. They cannot be too far removed from the living experience that they are designed to idealize and celebrate. The images they use must be recognizable and the values they glorify must be acceptable. A good religious myth will thus give shape to the values of the society that it serves by clothing them in aesthetic concreteness. Myths are in that sense derivative from, and dependent on, the values of the society. For the individual in the society, of course, they celebrate, glorify, and thus legitimate those same values.

To come back to still another form of the distinction I have been making throughout, then, religious myths and religious values are dependent on the social values of any given time, but the value of religious myth and the function of religious values are not so dependent. If social values change under the impact of technological change, as I have tried to demonstrate, the content of the myths in which they find their religious form must also change. But I have argued, further, that value change consequent on technological change has a discernible direction. It would therefore follow that religious mythology would also have to evolve in that same direction if it is to remain adequate to a changing society. If it does not succeed in doing so, it will leave a vacuum that some secular myth will seek to fill, either another cult like communism or some naive and superrationalistic scientism of the sort that writers like Jacques Ellul keep warning us about.

There is a challenge here to both the theologian and the pastor. The former needs to look to his stories, with one eye on the eternal verities and the other on the realities of modern technology. The latter will have to minister to the religious needs of his flock as the objects and values responsive to those needs change with changes in the society. The theologian is bound to fail if he misinterprets as literal the artistic truth of religious myth or if he loosens his hold on the eternal under the impact of rapid temporal change. The pastor will fail if he forgets his principally religious function in the heat of social action. Technological change no more threatens religion than it threatens values, in other words, but it does challenge it—as it does values—to remain adequate to the realities of contemporary religious experience.

* * *

DR. MEAD: My problem with Dr. Mesthene's paper is that it is extraordinarily abstract. I am interested in how we can bring it down more concretely to our own experience—perhaps more to the pastors than the theologians since the theologians can probably stay up there too.

When I was in the Admiralty Islands back in 1928 the people believed in the ghosts of their ancestors but they were also among the most pragmatic, down-to-earth, realistic people I had ever met.

They had no time whatsoever for cheap alibis. They asked little of their guardian ghost. They would only say, "Sir Ghost, if you see any fish around the other side of the island, would you send them this way?" They never asked him to make any fish. They were also very realistic people who learned to dismantle a diesel engine in two or three hours.

When I planned to go back to the Islands in 1963 I was told that under the impact of modern technology and of all the GI's who had come there during World War II, something had gone wrong. After becoming converted to Christianity, the people had developed a totally mystical cult, which is called a cardinal cult in the Pacific. They had moved inland and formed a religion made up half of the old ghosts and half of bulldozers, and they had lost the rather concrete and realistic relationship they previously had to their environment.

Now, before my return trip I tried to think back to what could have happened: Perhaps the new technology was too difficult for them. The people had been very, very efficient, however, in thinking about a typewriter, and they had worked hard. My typewriter was the first they had ever seen. The children had stood around it and said, "Now, first she pushes that and that comes up and that pushes on that long black strip and you get a mark. What's on that long black strip?" They asked only "how" questions, but they were able to cope with new technology very well. But it is possible that they couldn't cope with the new electronics, and in discouragement were thrown into a state of mystical confusion in which they had not been before.

When I finally arrived and actually talked to them, however, —to these people who had skipped over two thousand years in the brief span of twenty-five—I found that they weren't a bit worried by electronics. They distinguished between the animate and the inanimate, and they put a tape recorder in the animate and left the typewriter and anything that you would in the inanimate. They had no difficulty with these things at all. They said the trouble with American machines was that they had been put in boxes and you have only a start button and a stop button but no channel chart. They didn't use the words "channel chart," but they clearly referred to what the words meant. They said, "If we only knew what was inside the box we would have no trouble at all, but we don't know, and we like to think a little the way we did when we first saw the Ford: we could see perfectly well what it was and we knew how it worked. But these things we can't understand. If only we knew what was inside we would have no trouble." In other words, they were not flummoxed by any new technology, but they were flummoxed by a lack of relationship between what they knew how to work with, and what they were now trying to work with.

Now, what I would like to ask Dr. Mesthene is how we evaluate and what we do with the relationship between people's current state of intelligence and character and the technological state with which we are confronted. When we talk about the problem of technology we have to realize that it is over twenty years since the concept of cybernetics was made available to the thinking people of the United States, but it is only recently that it was adequately conceptualized and set up, made available to us so we could understand negative feedback and positive feedback and feed forward. Even to this present time we are incapable of building anything that deals with these problems. When the main power on a machine fails we build an auxiliary engine not attached to the main power supply. But we have not succeeded in making concrete for the human beings who have to use the present systems a relationship to the systems that will make such use possible for them.

Now, you stated very eloquently the relationship between society and the state of its values and the way these are related to the eternal, with which I would entirely agree. But I think our concrete problem is how do we build a society on the basis of linear sequence and a linear notion of cause and effect and machines that you wind up, when there is no recognition whatsoever within that society of the complex feedbacks that belong to the modern economy. Our problem is that today we have an entire population working on linear systems and with no allowance for feedback. That's what we have—in a society that depends completely on feedback for its existence. What do we do with a society that depends on feedback, as does the airport in Cincinnati? First, they put in a lovely door, with an electric eye. As you approach the door, it opens all right. But because it has been put in backwards, it now has a very large sign that says, "Door opens out—beware!"

DR. JONES: I know that if you looked at your program you will realize that in this whole group of academia I am the sole sport from industry. I accept that, but it leaves me in the predicament that I now find myself.

Let me very seriously, however, express our interests—my interest as a citizen and a member of industry—in this conference and in the questions it is seeking to explore. For indeed, we in industry have a great need for any leadership that can be provided in these areas.

Dr. Mesthene has given us an extremely scholarly dissertation on technology and values, and I suspect there is a good deal more in what he said than I, for one, picked up in just hearing his presentation. Let me move to the end of the spectrum and from the viewpoint of industry share with you briefly some of the problems that we see facing our society today—and thus facing us as purveyors of goods and services to that society.

First of all, I think we can accept the fact that technology is indeed a fact of today's life, and that it has developed without anybody planning for its complete integration into the society. In fact, it has literally burst upon us in this century of unparalleled energy. Its development has been uneven, but at the same time it is safe to say that we presently have the technology in hand that will be required to meet most of the human and societal needs that we face today. But by and large, technology's impact on society has been an unplanned one. We have reacted to the hardware and tc its impact on society, but not necessarily—perhaps very infrequently—to the ideas behind it. Man has not controlled the technological environment; on the contrary, he has been controlled by it: sometimes insulted by it, more often coddled by it, but nevertheless controlled.

Now, as Dr. Mesthene has pointed out, technology has indeed changed our ideas of value. With the improvement in technology and with the choices provided by the emergence of technology, there has not, unfortunately, come about a corresponding growth of human understanding. Speaking specifically of scientists and engineers—these are the people I know best—I think this is due, at least partially, to the fact that the intellectually elite by and large have had a segmented education. In effect, we have developed a segment of people coming from the engineering ghettos. You won't believe it, but I was trained as a chemical engineer. We are trained in the techniques, but not in the thoughts of technology.

In earlier years, perhaps a hundred or two hundred years ago, it was possible for a man to know practically everything the human race had learned up to that time. A man like Benjamin Franklin comes to mind. Physicians were also philosophers. Astronomers were also poets. But in today's world we have specialists. Unfortunately, technology has tended to take specialists farther and farther from the human base of life.

I might say further that some of the concern expressed by the students today is an attempt on their part to get some kind of handle on the technological world. To the extent that this is true, I am encouraged by this apparent awakening, this heightened effort on the part of the individual to control the environment. This in turn can be further heightened by more effective training, by the development of more complete people. For example, in the urbanologist now coming on the scene we have the first direct attempt to train a man in the technology necessary for handling human problems.

In industry we have developed a concern today for the need for more effective people to handle problems of the future. It is in industry that technology has had its greatest proliferation, and it is through technology and through management that industry has indeed contributed greatly to the material well-being of the people. We have come a long way toward making use of human beings.

But at the same time it is painfully apparent that the provision of better goods at lower prices is not enough. Along with our increase of material wealth has come a host of problems, for most of which we have no ready answer. But business must and does respond to human and social needs, and it does this to an unusual extent. This is our stock in trade.

Looking down the road, it seems evident to me that the world of tomorrow will reward those industrial ventures that demonstrate an awareness of their social responsibilities, and in doing so can count among their accomplishments not only material advances but continuing contributions to the dignity of the individual. In this respect we in industry will need the continuing help of the disciplines represented by the distinguished members of this entire conference.

Dr. Mesthene, I have no question to ask. I want to compliment you on your presentation. I want to urge that you continue your interest in enlisting common effort on matters of mutual concern as we translate technology into the areas of useful things for men while looking out at the same time for the entire spectrum of the needs of the human being.

DR. EVANS: This is a very important problem for those of us working in social psychology. As we listen to sociological, theological, and philosophical discourses on this problem, we see how critical sound analysis becomes.

We are very excited about looking at these broad institutional problems. We are also quite interested in the broader theological, philosophical, and sociological problems. But we continue to be concerned about a question that Sir Julian Huxley put before this campus some years ago. I remember hearing him say that perhaps the most serious problem facing the world today is the gap between technological development and the understanding of human competency in human relations. He said it is really quite incredible. And I remember that he drew a large thermometer on the board and showed how our technological development was way up, while down at the bottom was our development in human relations. A few years later I happened to be at a conference with him in London and asked if he still felt that the gap was so great. He said, "If anything, I feel this gap is even greater now."

So I decided for the fun of it—and as part of a National Science Foundation project in which we were doing a series of dialogues with the world's notable psychologists, psychiatrists, and psychoanalysts—to ask some distinguished contributors to the behavioral sciences about this gap and what hope they might have that it can be appreciably reduced. Among the people we asked were the late Karl Jung, Eric Fromm, Eric Erickson, and a good many others; also, most recently, Nella Sanford and playwright Arthur Miller.

There was an interesting consistency to their responses. Almost everyone said that if you look at this thing from a purely rational standpoint, the chances are that the gap cannot be well handled. By the way, one of the individuals also at that particular conference was the distinguished behavioral scientist at Harvard, B. F. Skinner. He felt as the other conference participants all felt, that the chances of the gap being reduced appreciably before the destruction of man, or before man seriously overpopulates the planet, are very slight. But then most of them also quite eloquently left the rational plane of discussion and said, "However, we can't continue to function on that assumption. We've got to continually assume that the gap can be overcome, and overcome rather rapidly."

Now, in listening to Dr. Mesthene's presentation, I was taken by the eloquence of the linguistic structure as he dealt with the attempt to see perhaps one way this problem could be solved. I was, however, very disappointed that the earlier promise of the paper, that made one feel that perhaps he would now lead us into a long-range projection for action, never came off. It is possible that this was due to lack of time. So my question to you, sir, is whether you have any projections to suggest for overcoming this gap?

DR. MESTHENE: I am not going to take all the time available to respond to the three comments. I would rather restrict myself to just a few comments, the purpose of which will be to indicate to you the direction my response would take if I took the time to respond.

Dr. Mead challenged me with hyperabstraction. But then, it seemed to me, in her illustration about the backward door and the black box of electronics and so forth and so on, she gave the most eloquent statement yet that when you get right down to it the most practical thing in the world is theoretical clarity, because if you don't have that, practice will go wrong. That is the direction in which I would couch my response to her.

Dr. Jones touched on a number of interests of mine. I have never met him before this meeting and he sounds like an extremely enlightened industrialist. The only thing I have not been able to determine is whether or not he is enlightened enough to realize that what he said was, in fact, that some of the problems that our modern technology is getting us into result from the fact that for many years we have left the determination of the direction of technological change to the market rather than to deliberate public decision.

He also said something about the gap, as did Mr. Evans—the gap between wisdom and technical capability. This is something that I have spent a fair amount of time thinking about and writing about. I am quite conscious of the gap. But I am also impressed, on the other hand, by the fact that for almost a quarter of a century we have had the capability to blow the whole world to kingdom come, yet have not done so. Perhaps the gap is not quite as wide as one might suspect.

Incidentally, with respect to Dr. Jones' point about social responsibility, with which I agree entirely, it should be pointed out that social responsibility on the part of the industrialists is quite old. It started with the dimes that John D. Rockefeller, Sr., used to dispense to the children who gathered around him. But the situation is different today—and here is where I would recommend that Dr. Jones read a very good friend and former colleague of mine, Carl Kaysen,[5] a professor of economics who sees that, in fact, social responsibility of industry will become a reality only when we find the social mechanisms to make it profitable; otherwise it means little more than distributing shiny dimes.

I don't know what to say to Dr. Evans. He said basically that he is disappointed in me, and I'm sorry. He said I didn't do everything that he hoped I would do, which of course I didn't.

QUESTIONER: Dr. Mesthene, your remark about the direction of technological change being left to the market place brought to my mind the matter of how our TV programs are directed. A question arises as to who will direct this technological change: some supermind, or will it be the voters, the common people in the market place? What are we doing about Vietnam? Who is to decide? The superman in Washington who knows—or the man in the street? And finally, how are we going to get this knowledge to the people if it is they who in the last analysis must lead the change?

DR. MESTHENE: Well, I'm not going to get involved in Vietnam. I think you have put your finger on, in a sense, what is the crucial question of our time. But I suspect that you have misformulated it just a little bit and I would like to illustrate the distinction I see between what I think is your slight misformulation and the way your question probably is more usefully formulated.

In the program that I direct at Harvard one of the projects we have under way is on the social-ethical-political implications of the advances in biomedical technology. Several of the people in the group that is working on this subject attended a meeting not long

[5] See Carl Kaysen, "The Business Corporation as a Creator of Values," in Sidney Hook, *op. cit.*, pp. 209-223.

ago in which we were talking about the value—the intellectual research value—of undertaking a project to evaluate the problems or to identify and formulate the problems that would arise. We sought to discern the political, ethical, and social problems that might ensue when current research is finally able to control human behavior, whether by way of physical means such as Delgado's experiments at Yale involving the insertion of electrodes in the brain, or by chemical means with drugs, or by sociological means à la Skinner rites. A dispute arose when all of the medical people present started pooh-poohing my suggestions. I thought the question was certainly worth looking into, but they said, "My god, that's so far away it's not worth inquiring into." "Well," I asked them, "how far? Let's take the year 2000. What probability would you assign to the following proposition: that by the year 2000, which is only thirty-two years away, we will have the technical capabilities to control within significant limits the behavior of significant groups of people. I don't mean whole countries, but we might be able to control the behavior of prisoners within prisons or of inmates in mental hospitals." One colleague thought the chances were about "fifty-fifty." I said, "Are you giving me your professional opinion that within thirty-two years there is the probability of .5 that we will have the techniques—the scientific techniques—available to control human behavior?" He replied, "Yes, I am." I said, "Well, you know you have given me the most eloquent reason yet for why we should start looking into these questions now."

And in response—and now I'm coming directly to your question—he replied, "All right, suppose we decide who's going to make the decisions in the year 2,000—then what?"

Now in that response I think he misformulated the question in a way analogous to the way in which you have perhaps misformulated yours. The question is not really who decides *now* what decisions will be made thirty or thirty-two or ten or twenty years from now. The principal intellectual problem is rather to try to develop and do the research necessary to achieve an intelligent development of the mechanisms by which such decisions will eventually be made.

To illustrate this—and in order to answer my critics who argue that I am always too abstract—I will pick up your question about the market. I think your illustration about TV is very appropriate.

Here is a case in which the market mechanism basically decides what goes on the air, educational networks and PBL's aside for the moment.

Or take another example: the direction that science and technology take, which is what Dr. Jones talked about. Up to now the direction of technology has been the resultant—in the mathematical sense of the term—of individual decisions made by individual entrepreneurs; it has been set by whatever all those individual decisions added up to. This is the essence of the market mechanism. As a matter of fact, technology is now becoming far too expensive for individual entrepreneurs or individual companies or private organizations of any sort to be able to engage in it. Witness the aerospace industry; witness the supersonic transport; witness the commercial satellite. Any one of these projects is now beginning to require public funds. The moment public funds become involved the question arises about the mechanisms of public decision that are going to determine the way in which these funds are to be spent. At that point you move away from the impersonal market mechanism into a planned decision-making process.

QUESTIONER: I'd like to ask a question from the theological side. I thought I was following with some comprehension your analysis, but I found myself totally unprepared for the reference toward the end of your speech to eternal verities. My question is, where in your analysis of the nature and origin of value and valuing in the social order does this concept arise? What is the relationship between the eternal verities and values as you were using the term, or religious values?

DR. MESTHENE: Well, I don't want to make a long speech, so let me try to recall some of the things I said along the way. I made a distinction between particular values on the one hand and the function of values or the enterprise of valuing on the other hand.

There is a common arithmetical analogy. Two oranges plus two oranges are perishable and certainly temporal and non-eternal. But the formula two plus two is certainly eternal. I use the term "eternal" incidentally, in the literal sense of the term, meaning that time is not relevant. Eternal does not mean unchanging or something forever lasting; eternal means time is not relevant to it. Time and social circumstance are relevant to the concept of particular values, both social and religious. Time is not relevant to the being of and the functioning of social and religious values. As long as there are men living together on earth, the enterprise of valuing will be meaningful and eternal, in the sense of being independent of time.

I find that too many theologians think that doing theology is the same thing as doing sociology. This was the basis upon which I addressed my remark, and what I am arguing is that it is the job of the theologian to investigate the relationship that is embodied in the term "religious value." He works irrespective of the content of the particular set of religious values at any particular time. To do that is to keep your eye on the eternal verity in the sense that I use it.

All value has its genesis in choice behavior. In other words, the choice behavior of human beings is a condition sine qua non for the existence of values in any sense of the term—in the psychologist's sense, in the sociologist's sense, in the philosopher's sense, in the theologian's sense, or what have you. The term "value" cannot be understood except as a function of choice behaviors.

That is where I started from, and starting from that point I distinguish the different senses of value—and one of the easiest ways to distinguish them is to identify them with the differences between the various disciplines that concern themselves with them. The sociologist is concerned with values in one sense as descriptive abstractions or generalizations of different choice patterns observable in a particular society. The moral philosopher is concerned with more than that; he is concerned not only with what this society values, but whether this society or these people in this society are right: is it good for them to value what they value or should they be valuing something else? That is another aspect of value.

Now, in addition to these two aspects, there are certainly other aspects which I have not considered. I have not considered aesthetic value, although I alluded to it in passing, and I have not considered value in the psychologist's sense of the term. But taking off from these two conceptions of value, the descriptive conception of the sociologist and the prescriptive conception of the moral philosopher, I then argue that as you go one step further in abstraction you come to the dual constituents of the religious value. One is the abstraction of good and evil into ultimates and the other the embodiment of social value into mythology, which tends to legitimate or clothe or celebrate the social values in which the religious mythology operates.

Part Two

ILLUSTRATIVE PROBLEMS

3. Abortion and the Law

The conference opened with general sessions dealing with the broad cultural and philosophical issues that provide the context of any meaningful discussion of ethics in medicine and technology. Following this, it focused its attention on the first of a series of very specific problems. The bridge between cultural, biological, and theological concern was embodied and forcefully articulated by Dean Robert Drinan. The session at which he spoke vividly developed what the recent International Conference on Abortion called "the most devastating moral question of our time."[1]

The problem of abortion has indeed been magnified to the point of critical importance in recent years. Increasing social pressure to legitimatize and legalize the procedure has been accompanied by strong counterreaction from the religious communities which oppose abortion. In this country several states have followed the lead of England and of the eastern European countries in a new legalization of abortion under certain conditions. The California, Colorado, and North Carolina statutes have provoked wide debate.

Dean Drinan, an internationally recognized authority on abortion and the law, has appeared on briefs in significant cases of medical-ethical import before the Supreme Court of the United States. A contributor to many journals and author of Religion, The Courts, and Public Policy,[2] *Dr. Drinan is currently dean of the Boston College Law School. The printed version of his remarks is a composite of his prepared paper and his delivered address.*

Responses to Dean Drinan's presentation were offered by Dean John Neibel of the University of Houston Law School; Dr. William Cantrell,

---

[1] See Robert E. Cooke et al., eds., *The Terrible Choice: The Abortion Dilemma* (New York: Bantam Books, 1968), Preface. This volume is based on the proceedings of the International Conference on Abortion sponsored by the Harvard Divinity School and the Joseph P. Kennedy Jr. Foundation.

[2] Robert Drinan, *Religion, the Courts, and Public Policy* (New York: McGraw Hill, 1963).

Department of Psychiatry, Baylor College of Medicine; and Dr. Paul Ramsey, a theologian whose own address to the conference appears in the next chapter.

Abortion and the Law

Robert F. Drinan, S.J.

I am always impressed by the Texas Medical Center, but all I can think of today is that if the doctors, geneticists, and biologists worked harder we wouldn't have to talk about abortion any longer. They would invent a pill or injection or something by which a woman would know exactly the twenty-four or forty-eight hours in each cycle when she ovulates or when she is fertile. And if they wanted to be imaginative they could even provide a side effect whereby she would turn a certain color during those hours, like "red, stop!" Since they are not working hard enough, moral theologians still have a bit of a problem, along with the lawyers!

I am not here as a Catholic or as a priest, but, I guess, as a grown-up fetus! I do want to stress this point before getting into my deposition or my exploration or analysis of the law and the three options available to the law. I want to say that this is not a Catholic problem. It is something in which all of us are involved, and obviously it is very, very serious.

I commend the founders of this very prestigious, important, and influential Institute of Religion, and although all of the other problems are agonizing and crucial, it seems to me that in the next five or ten years the whole question of abortion could tear this country apart. It could affect our foreign policy. It could have a very serious effect on intercreedal relations, which now are so ecumenical and sweet.

This is not, I repeat, a Catholic problem; it is not a case of the Catholic against the world, as is suggested very often in the mass media and by individuals. If I may, I want to suggest to you that all Protestant and Jewish bodies, as well as nonreligious groups, feel very deeply that a fetus should not be aborted except for grave medical or other very serious reasons.

Areas of Agreement

Catholics are well known for their position, which may indeed be more consistent or logical than some other positions. Father Bernard Häring, a renowned contemporary moral theologian, minimizes the probability of the theory of mediate animation when he writes in *The Law of Christ* that today "the view that the soul is infused *immediately* at the moment of conception is almost universally accepted by physicians and especially by theologians." The theory of *mediate* animation, inherited from Aristotle by way of Aquinas, Father Häring categorizes as "only slightly probable," stating that "it is utterly untenable at least on the practical moral level."[3]

Holding apparently a position somewhat different from that of Father Häring is Father Richard McCormick, S.J.: "The theory of retarded or delayed animation is unquestionably a tenable and respectable theory. It is still preferred by a notable number of philosophers and theologians. The Church has very wisely never decided the matter definitively; indeed, it is perhaps questionable if this is within her competence."[4]

Now let us look at the problem. How many illegal abortions are there each year? We have a monumental ignorance about this. There may be two hundred thousand, perhaps a million two hundred thousand. Take your choice. We are operating in the dark about the impact, if any, of the law in this area. I suggest to you that more dialogue, like the one we are having just now, should and must take place. Why? Because Protestants and Catholics, in my estimation, are not as far apart as the press may seem to indicate.

Here is what the National Council of Churches said in 1961: "All Christians are agreed in condemning abortions or any method which destroys human life except when the health or life of the mother is at stake. And the destruction of life already begun cannot

[3] Bernard Häring, *The Law of Christ* (Westminster, Md.: Newman, 1966), pp. 73 ff.

[4] See *America* 112 (19 June 1965): 879.

be condoned as a method of family limitation." The Episcopalians or Anglicans at Lambeth have said more or less the same thing. Other church groups in this country have reiterated this position that abortion may be justified only for the most serious medical reason.[5]

Let me quote a well-known sentence from the famous Karl Barth: "The unborn child is from the very first a child. It is still developing and has no independent life. But it is a man and not a thing, not a mere part of the mother's body. . . . He who destroys germinating life kills a man and thus ventures a monstrous thing of decreeing concerning the life and death of a fellow man, whose life is given to him by God, and therefore, like his own, belongs to Him."[6]

Dietrich Bonhoeffer, the heroic Christian executed by the Nazis, is even more forceful. In his *Ethics* he writes: "Destruction of the embryo in the mother's womb is a violation of the right to live, which God has bestowed upon this nascent life. . . . The simple fact is that God certainly intended to create a human being and that this nascent human being has been deliberately deprived of his life. And that is nothing but murder."[7]

The distinguished Protestant theologian, Helmut Thielicke, who is also addressing this conference, has said that abortion involves the question "whether an already bestowed gift can be spurned, whether one dares to brush aside the arm of God after this arm has already been outstretched. Therefore, here [in abortion] the order of creation is infringed upon in a way that is completely different from that of the case of contraception."[8]

I could quote other Protestants, as well as non-Protestants, but my point is simply this: As a Christian I welcome the opportunity to try to explore and analyze those differences which do, in fact,

---

[5] For statements and analysis of Protestant positions on abortion see "Contemporary Protestant Thinking" by Robert F. Drinan, S.J. in *America* 117 (9 December 1967): 713 ff.

[6] Karl Barth, *Church Dogmatics*, ed. G. W. Bromiley and T. F. Torrance (Edinburgh: T. & T. Clark, 1961), III[4], 415-16.

[7] Dietrich Bonhoeffer, *Ethics*, ed. Eberhard Bethge, trans. Neville Horton Smith (New York: Macmillan Co., 1955), pp. 175-76.

[8] Helmut Thielicke, *The Ethics of Sex*, trans. John W. Doberstein (New York: Harper and Row, 1964), p. 227.

exist between Catholic and Protestant moral traditions, but also to explore those things which unite us.

As regards the Jewish position, I think it would be fair to say that it involves a reverent and responsible attitude toward the question of abortion. The tendency of Jewish law is to permit abortion in grave situations. Reasons of convenience are not admissible. Reasons affecting basic life and health may sanction abortion; but public policy ought to protect the morality threatened by easy abortion and at the same time protect the well-being of mother and child when adequate justification for abortion prevails.[9]

What are some of the nonissues, those things on which we all agree? Catholics would agree and no one, I assume, would have any objection in the case where the fetus is conceived in the Fallopian tube. An ectopic pregnancy may be excised, and if there is an abortion involved here it is unintended. This procedure can be justified in the very rare cases where that happens. Similarly, if the woman has cancer of the uterus, and the only way of stopping the metastases is by removing the uterus, and thereby indirectly performing an abortion or destroying an embryo or fetus, then that is permitted under what Catholics call the principle of the double effect.

Secondly, I think that we are all agreed that abortion should never be substituted for birth control. In Japan, when abortion was legalized in the early fifties, it was an attempt at controlling the population. I think that we would agree that there should be publicly financed clinics, responsible parenthood courses, and so on, so that abortion would not be indulged in as a method of birth control. Similarly, everybody agrees that we are talking only about the nonviable child, that is, the embryo or fetus prior to the twentieth or twenty-fourth week.

I think also there is some agreement in the agonizing cases of rape and incest. Both Catholic and Protestant theology would say that a pregnancy may be prevented after a rape or incest. On the theory that the assaulted woman can resist the unjust aggressor, she may, prior to pregnancy (possibly up to five days after rape or

[9] See, e.g., Immanuel Jakobovits, *Jewish Medical Ethics* (New York: Bloch, 1959), pp. 190-91.

incest) take appropriate measures to prevent a pregnancy. At least we are agreed that in these areas there is some consensus among us.

Similarly we are agreed that the horrible statistics you read in the popular magazines, about the alleged number of deaths of women from illegal abortions, are greatly exaggerated. In the last known year, three years ago, there were two hundred seventy-six deaths in America from all types of abortion, legal and illegal; Dr. Christopher Tietze has verified this and he is an international expert on that particular question.[10]

The Laws on Abortion

What shall we do about this whole problem, therefore, in the law? I would digress for a moment to say that the immorality of abortion is not merely something that we know from Judaism or from Christianity. I think all of us should be reminded that Roman law, prior to Christianity, made abortion a very serious crime. The penalty was often though not always the same as for infanticide. It is clear, however, that both Christianity and Judaism intensified and deepened the respect which we have for the sanctity of fetal life.

Why is it, then, that there should be as great an issue in the law as there now is? As you know, three states last year legalized abortion in a limited way, and Georgia apparently is about to legalize it. England has a law which I think became effective April 1, which is more liberal—more lax, if you will—than any law in western culture. It appears to legalize abortion on request.

Catholic moral teaching on the issue is rather clear: Vatican II said that abortion is an unspeakable crime. I do not think that necessarily solves the problem of the law for a Catholic. What, therefore, shall we say about the law?

In America today we have a law which came to us from an updated version of the law ratified by Parliament in 1802—a Parliament from which, incidentally, all Roman Catholics were excluded by law. That law decreed that abortion under any circumstance is a serious offense. Both the woman and the doctor

[10] See Cooke et al., *op. cit.*, p. xiii. Dr. Tietze serves in the Bio-Medical Division of The Population Council with headquarters in New York City.

and any accomplice could be severely punished. There is one exception in the law in every state, namely, that the life of the mother is a justifying reason for abortion. Last year there were some eight thousand *legal* abortions performed in hospitals by doctors who signed their names and stipulated that the woman's life was in danger. That eight thousand also includes the five states where the health or safety of the mother is a legitimate reason for doing an abortion. The state of Maryland has a law which makes the "safety" of the mother a justifying cause. The result is that Johns Hopkins and other hospitals in that state do abortions.

Three Options

Is the present system a good thing? There are only three ways by which we can treat this whole matter in the law: You can have the present system of outlawing abortion, thereby making it illegal; you can have what three or four states now have, the Model Penal Code; or you can withdraw penal sanctions. I would like to explore each of these with you and show you that all we can hope for is the least unsatisfactory solution and that there are advantages and disadvantages with each of these three options.

The Present System

The present system has some advantages. It says categorically in our law that we protect all life, from the womb to the tomb, and that no individual has the right to take the life of another person, however convenient this taking might be for the individual to whom the existence of another is a bother. The one exception is the life of the mother. You could justify that by saying that the infant or fetus is an unjustified aggressor when it poses a threat to the very life of the mother.

Aside from that one case (which practically never happens any more), the present law forbids all abortions and treats the fetus as a person, as an inchoate being, a potential human being who has the right to be born. The law says in effect that the parents or mother have a duty to bring this child into the world. Is the fact that this law is rather unenforceable a reason in and of itself to justify the repeal of it? That is one norm by which we should evaluate laws, but there are many laws which are unenforceable and if we are going to use the criterion of unenforceability as the one norm, then we have a lot of work to do in repealing laws like the antiliquor laws in Texas and elsewhere.

Public authorities today are generally unable or unwilling to carry out the enforcement of existing antiabortion laws. When the common convictions or the moral consensus which originally supported a law of a penal nature have eroded, it is sometimes wise for the law to withdraw its sanctions rather than have the majesty of the law brought into disrepute by open disobedience and unpunished defiance.

This conclusion is supported by the reasoning of Father John Courtney Murray, who writes: " . . . the aspirations of law are minimal. Law seeks to establish and maintain only that minimum of actualized morality that is necessary for the healthy functioning of the social order. . . . It enforces only what is minimally acceptable, and in this sense socially necessary. . . . Therefore the law, mindful of its nature, is required to be tolerant of many evils that morality condemns."[11] Applying these principles to the present nonenforcement of America's abortion laws one could urge a recommendation for the repeal of those laws.

We have many areas of human life where it is very difficult to control conduct, such as in prostitution. Obviously this is clandestine and surreptitious, but no one is suggesting we repeal all law in this area. People say we need social controls on gambling. This goes on in a surreptitious way, but no one is suggesting that we remove all social controls, because we know that men and women are weak and that they would be tempted to waste their week's wages on gambling. But despite the fact that the law contains severe penalties illegal gambling still goes on, and despite the violation of the law most observers feel that it is better to have a stated control of gambling than to have no control at all.

Likewise, we have divorces granted almost by consent. We do not do it by postcard exactly. We could, if we so desired, admit divorce by consent and just drop a registered letter, but society insists that we go through the practice of bringing people in and having grounds and so on. We have an instinctive feeling that we need a social control on all these things. Is abortion in that category? I

[11] John Courtney Murray, *We Hold These Truths* (New York: Doubleday, 1964), pp. 164-65.

suggest to you that one can make a very plausible argument that it is.

Law, furthermore, is more important in the United States than, I think, in any other pluralistically divided country. We do not have other symbols beside the law. The law is becoming more and more the norm of our public morality; if a thing is not forbidden by law then people assume that it is permissible.

Other nations have a symbol of their unity in a public heritage. England has the queen, France has De Gaulle, and Scandinavia has a language or culture. But I am afraid that in a religiously divided and culturally pluralistic country such as America, the law has assumed such enormous importance that a change in the law teaches people.

That is the case for the present situation. One could argue that it is a basic compromise to change the law and to deny a particular fetus the right to be born. I can argue that position by metaphysics and by emotion. Catholics are quite good at this. Bishops make passionate pleas and statements, and I am afraid that rhetoric is going to continue. Am I happy with the present situation? Well, I am not filing any bills to change it exactly. My initial feeling is that we have a monumental ignorance about this whole question.

The International Conference on Abortion, held last September in Washington, brought out for me and many others the fact that we have virtually no hard data or information on this question.[12] Even the very number of illegal abortions is unknown. Nor do we know who does them or who gets them. All this is a great mystery. So until we have more knowledge, I really could not write a law that would be more satisfactory than the present situation. My own intuition at the present is to say that we have enough laws. Thus, I say that you can make out a case for the first option, the present situation. At least I think that this is clearly better than the second option, which I am going to touch on now, though it is debatable whether it is better than the third option, the withdrawal of criminal sanctions.

The Model Penal Code

What is the second option? This is the proposal that is now in the legislatures of some fifteen or twenty states. It is the law

---

[12] See p. 51, n. 1 above.

that was adopted by three states last year. It was constructed by the American Law Institute, a group of prestigious jurists, 750 of them from all over the country, who meet annually and write such things as the Model Penal Code and statutes about commercial law. As a member of the American Law Institute I participated in the hammering out of the Model Penal Code, and I saw the anguish and the agony which the members experienced in coming to a compromise position on abortion. A compromise was the intention from the beginning. It was hoped that the Model Penal Code would get away from the strict absolute Draconian law which we have now and yet not sanction abortion by request. The Model Penal Code, finally ratified in 1961, gives three reasons why the mother should be able to have an abortion.

1) The first one is the physical or mental health of the mother. Should this be a reason set forth in the law why an abortion is permissible? Assuming that the doctors worked a little harder, we could have a predictive table of how many years a woman would live if she had the abortion and if she did not. Let us assume that a woman has a physical health problem and that the doctor could say to her, "If you have an abortion you will live to be seventy-two. If you continue the pregnancy you will die at sixty-two." Should the law then say that she can prefer ten years of her life to the very existence of her fetus? That is the challenge. That is the dilemma.

I am firmly opposed to putting that in the law. That is absolute expediency and utilitarianism, if not pragmatism. Such a law would teach that a woman may decide that her health, her future, her well-being is much more important than the very existence of her child. It seems to me that this is a devastating and a totally unprecedented principle to put into the law.

What about mental health? The psychiatrists whom I have read and with whom I have had dialogue say that most mental illness is totally unrelated to pregnancy. It does not come because of pregnancy and it will not go away if the pregnancy is terminated. It might be aggravated or diminished by the pregnancy. In other words, the correlation between these two phenomena is very tricky and, although psychiatrists are not necessarily opposed to an abortion being allowed when the mental health of a mother might be damaged, they say that actual mental illness in this situation is a very rare thing. It appears that the reasons for the damage to the physical and mental health of mothers arising from pregnancy are decreasing and diminishing all the time and that, with adequate medicine, the physical and mental health of the mother will not be destroyed by the continuation of a pregnancy. Now I am not posing as a doctor and I realize that the evidence is in dispute. But I suggest to you that, however doctors—or women—might feel about it, I am opposed to inserting this in the law for the reasons I mention.

2) The second reason in the Model Penal Code is rape or incest. In other words, in these terribly tragic circumstances, the law would say that an abortion can be performed if there is sufficient evidence that the child was the product of rape or incest. Legally or jurisprudentially I do not have much difficulty with that. In this most difficult case I would not oppose a liberalization of the law. The important condition is that these cases be verified and that the alleged rape is not an illusion or fiction of the particular woman who wants an abortion.

3) The third reason for abortion in the Model Penal Code is the predictably defective or deformed child. I have a great deal of difficulty morally and jurisprudentially with this. In effect, this law, or proposed law, would say that we have enough ugly Americans now and that we can therefore destroy damaged, defective, retarded, or deformed fetuses and embryos.

We must ask: What is so terrible about these people? Some would reply that such persons are going to be a drag on humanity and that their parents have a right to a perfect child. Now, I do not want to overload this argument, because I am urging all people to keep their options open with regard to the predictably deformed child. But I do not think this is a medical reason; it is a eugenic reason and clearly it is a social reason. Should the law say to these individuals that, if you do not want a retarded child or if you do not want a child who may be deformed a bit, then you can dispose of this fetus and hope that you will have a perfect blue-eyed baby in your next pregnancy?

This seems to be a very negative thing, first of all. It does not do justice to the whole new science of fetology which makes it possible for defects in fetuses to be corrected by surgery or other treatment. The law, moreover, cannot realistically indicate the level of certainty which would be required before you can abort.

Furthermore, what about the level or the degree or the intensity of defectiveness or retardation that is required? Would just a little retardation or just a little bit of deformity—a club foot perhaps—be sufficient? I have a great deal of difficulty with that particular eugenic argument. It seems to me that the argument *is* eugenic, that is, it suggests the selection of the strong or the destruction of the weak. For that very reason we should keep our minds open.

Apparently very little is known about the reasons for involuntary miscarriages, and this gives rise to a great problem for moral theologians. If it became certain that 60 to 70 percent of all of the miscarriages occurred because of defective or deformed fetuses, would this fact suggest that nature intends to expel all malformed or misformed fetuses? And even if that is so (and this is *not* supported by empirical scientific knowledge) could you say that, when we are certain that this nonviable fetus is substantially defective, deformed, or retarded, we could help nature do what nature wants to do—namely, expel it? I suggest to you that there is a large question here and that no one should have an absolute categorical way of forbidding an abortion under those circumstances.

This third reason mentioned by the Model Penal Code gives me great trouble because it seems to teach that defective and retarded people are no good to society, that they do not produce and that we really should not have them around. Actually, I am very grateful for these people who have afflictions: They have made me more virtuous; they have made me more grateful to God for the absence of defects. I think therefore, that before we indulge in "fetal euthanasia," which is Dr. Ramsey's term,[13] it would be best for us to say that the world is filled with imperfect, but nonetheless loveable people. Before we say that we will not allow any more defective persons to come into existence, we had better get our moral principles very clear.

Withdrawal of Penal Sanctions

What now about the third option? I have told you about the present situation and argued both for it and against it. I have told

---

[13] See Paul Ramsey, "The Sanctity of Life," *The Dublin Review*, Spring 1967, pp. 3-23.

you about the second option and I am afraid I have not said much in favor of it. Now I come to the third option, that there be a complete withdrawal of the law from this area.

The American Civil Liberties Union has taken a position which apparently says there should be no criminal sanctions on the question of abortion.[14] They justify that position by a variety of arguments. They seek to protect the privacy of the married couple, the right of the woman to dispose of the fetus as she sees fit, and the right of the doctor to practice medicine as he feels he should. In using these arguments they do not prescind from the moral issue; they just say there should be no law in this area. They say people can and should do what they want without interference from the law.

One's evaluation of this third option depends upon what one judges to be the problem. The problem is apparently that 80 percent of our abortions in America are given to married women who simply do not want a third, fourth, or fifth child. This situation is not a medical problem; it is a social problem. It is simply the problem of the unplanned and unwanted pregnancy. Doctors say that women seeking an abortion are often uncertain whether they should have an abortion or whether they should have the child. There are pressures from all sides. The husband is upset at the unplanned pregnancy. Psychiatrists have testified that the woman in this predicament is under duress, even coercion, to abort the unwanted pregnancy. Many suggest that it is not really the mother's wish, but the wish of the father, to avoid this rude interruption in their well-made plans. Apparently, this is not only a problem of the poor. These women live in Scarsdale and Grosse Point. They should be able to plan their family, but they are unwilling or unable to prevent an unplanned pregnancy.

According to this third option, the withdrawal of criminal sanctions would help these particular women and other women—unwed mothers, for example—who just do not want to have this child. What happens to them under the present situation? Apparently they go off to illegal abortionists, where some of them get ill, and a few even die.

---

[14] See the newsletter of the ACLU, 1967 to date, esp. the newsletter of 25 March 1968.

The problem of illegal and unregulated abortions cannot be denied. For the sake of discussion let us assume the median figure of five hundred thousand abortions a year. One-fourth or more are probably done by licensed physicians. Should we legalize all abortions and say we will not force these women to be criminals? Let me set forth the arguments on this, pro and con, and then suggest some conclusions.

Under the situation envisaged by this third option, abortion would no longer be a crime. Such a system has the obvious benefit that the state does not decide who will live and who will die. This is really better in my judgment than the Model Penal Code, because here the law does not say that no ugly Americans need be born. The law says simply, "This is a matter for your private morality." This would take a lot of unenforceable laws off the books. It would negate all the laws surrounding abortion, so that, for example, selling the instruments for abortion would no longer be a crime. We could provide counseling for the woman; perhaps mandatory counseling and a cooling-off period, so that she would not be able to go to a doctor on a Tuesday afternoon and have the abortion within an hour or two; she would have to talk to somebody. I think the law should also provide that the father must have knowledge, be consulted, and give his consent. It seems to me that it would be very wrong to allow women to secure an abortion without the advice and consent of the father of the child.

Thus the withdrawal of criminal sanctions might actually meet the social problems which exist. It would clearly protect the privacy of marriage and the claimed right of parents to dispose of a fetus as they see fit.

But what are the disadvantages of withdrawing criminal sanctions? Would we not be saying in effect that although we will protect everybody's life, you have to be viable to claim this protection. In other words, for the first twenty weeks, anybody's existence would be beyond the pale of the law. They have civil privileges, they may inherit property, and, once they are born they may recover for prenatal injuries, but we will not protect their lives by means of criminal sanctions. Is not this saying in effect that they are not human beings with the right to life, liberty, and the pursuit of human happiness?

And what results might follow if we were to do that? Would there be an erosion of the profound respect which society and the law and all of us have for the sanctity of life? If we say that fetal life is not really worth protecting, or that we cannot protect it or choose not to protect it, would that attitude escalate to the point of withdrawal, minimization, and shrinking of our public protection of life?

Second, would this lead to an escalation in the number of abortions? In every country where abortion has been liberalized there has occurred an escalation in the number of abortions. People say, "Well, it's legal now." In Scandinavia they do not necessarily go through the regular machinery, but it is done. Why? Well, because it is permitted. The law teaches that it is perfectly all right. If the law withdrew, would people infer that it is perfectly all right now? That is clearly one of the potential disadvantages of this third option.

Third, would it damage the whole movement for responsible parenthood? The level of contraceptive information is probably higher in America than in any other country of the world. The people who are now planning only that number of children which they can adequately care for and educate is higher then ever before. If we were to say now that abortion is permitted as a kind of a second line of defense in case contraception fails, would that tend to slow this whole movement for responsible parenthood? As a spinoff of that, would abortion, if it were freely available, become the chief birth control method of the poor? In other words, where the poor and uneducated couple have difficulty in planning their family, a social welfare agency, in good faith and seeking to help them, might say, "Why don't you have an abortion instead of bearing this sixth or seventh child?" This is a clear possibility. But the real imponderable, it seems to me, is this: Would the repeal of abortion laws diminish the profound respect which all of us have for the sanctity of life?

A fourth and final disadvantage of the third option is this: this proposal takes the whole matter and says to the M.D.'s of America, "Here, it's your problem." I have talked to medical associations and have concluded that doctors, in my judgment, do not want the criminal sanctions against abortion removed. They want some guidelines. They want to know what abortions they can do and what abortions they cannot do. It's quite understandable that they say, "I can't find time in my practice to give guidance and counseling to a woman and help her make a decision about an abortion. I want and need some legal standard."

At the International Conference on Abortion in Washington, a distinguished physician, who identified himself as a nonbeliever, said in his fine British accent, "I will not do abortions. I will do abortions for medical reasons, but I will not do abortions for social reasons. I, as a doctor, heal and save life. I do not destroy life." He went on to give a solemn warning: "Do not give this problem to the doctors, because you will lose your faith in the doctors if they begin to destroy life on your request. Destroying life is not the function of a doctor." This is a very profound statement. It relates to the faith of the public in the integrity of the medical profession, a theme already developed here by Margaret Mead.

Conclusion

There are several issues of concern that I have not yet touched upon. The one that bothers me considerably is what this struggle means for intercreedal tensions or conflicts. When I see the New York Council of Churches make a statement in favor of liberalization of the law (the Blumenthal Law), and when I see Catholic bishops make a statement on the other side to the effect that the law should not be changed at all, whether in Colorado or California, I just wonder whether we as Christians cannot get together and say that we have to have some type of consensus on this. How inhibiting it is to Christian unity when Protestant Christians say one thing and Catholic Christians say something else about a very complex fundamental legal and moral question. Granted, the Catholic theology or tradition is clearer on this, and the Catholics may be better organized; but Catholics are in a painful situation on this question and I ask, therefore, for your empathy and, if you will, your compassion.

In effect, Catholics are sometimes accused in this area of violating the civil rights of others or trying to impose their own morality on individuals who may disagree with them. This is not a very pleasant charge to have hurled at you. I know well how deeply people outside the Catholic church feel that the Catholic church is unfairly insisting that the public morality now embodied in the law remain. I say, however, that there must be some type of civilized way by which Christians can talk together; and I ask you in this community, and elsewhere, to continue to talk, because if we do not talk about abortion, there will be intercreedal scars which will remain for a long time to come.

Maybe I am being naive or unrealistic about this, because Catholics and Protestants do not even talk about bus rides for parochial schools. Wherever this issue comes up there is a great religious war again. So if we cannot talk about bus rides, how can we talk about abortion? I say to you that here is a fundamental question where public morality and Christian ethics are involved. I do hope that we can have more dialogue and sympathy and a feeling of respect for the integrity and for the motives of one another.

I suggest to you that this whole struggle is not going to go away; it will be here for a long time. I am afraid that I will have to be talking about it for some time to come. This is a very serious problem of conscience for Catholics.

It seems to me that the bishops of Canada made probably the most sophisticated statement on the problem.[15] They said that Catholic doctrine and what Catholics hold to be really basic morality applicable to everybody is very clear. A child is a child and, quoting Vatican II, it is an unspeakable crime to destroy the embryo for the mere convenience of the mother or father. They went on to say, however, that they did not know which legal arrangement would minimize the number of fetal deaths. They explored the three options I have given you and they said that we leave this to the legislators and conscientious people to figure out, by a democratic process, which is best for the common good.

I say in conclusion that the basic centerpiece of all law and of our morality has been the untouchability and the inviolability of every human being by any other human being for his own convenience or benefit. However convincing, compelling, and convenient the arguments in favor of abortion may be, we must insure the basic right to life. Certainly we have tragic cases; we have lives ruined. The fact remains, and we must always come back to this, that the taking of a life, even though it is only the fetal life, must

[15] See the monthly issues of the *Catholic Mind* for 1967 and 1968.

be justified. If we say that easy abortion can be justified then we really cut the heart out of the basic principle in our jurisprudence that no one's life, however unwanted, however useless it may be, may be terminated simply to promote the happiness or health of another human being.

And if the advocates of legalized abortion really want an intellectually honest debate, they cannot skirt the question of whether life is there or not. Nor can they evade this question by saying that it is up to the couple or the mother or the doctor. They have to face the fact that the fetus is a thing that has some rights; it may not be a full-blown human being, but they have to face the fact that it has been protected in our law. They cannot say that the law should be repealed simply because it is unenforceable. Since they cannot prove that a fetus is mere protoplasm, they must accept the fact they are opting for a different standard of values, a standard which assumes that the rights of the living are more powerful than the rights of those unseen.

This is the inescapable moral issue in the emerging struggle over the wisdom and fairness of American abortion laws. In my humble judgment it would be a tragedy beyond description if this problem were settled on the basis of sentimental emotion or expediency rather than in terms of the basic ethical issue involved. That ethical issue is this: the immorality of the destruction of any human being by more powerful human beings merely for the sake of their own convenience, power, or comfort.

* * *

DEAN NEIBEL: May I point out that in the basic theme of Father Drinan's talk he, as a skilful orator, has placed the issue in the context most favorable to himself and stated that the issue is the quantity of life. We need not accept that major premise, which has not been articulated clearly by him. The alternative issue, of course, is that concerning the quality of life.

And the Catholics are in tough shape on this issue, it seems to me, because originally they took the position that any unnatural interference with the life process is immoral. This position has now changed and they seem to have worked their morality around to accepting it. Thus, artificial insemination is all right, operating on the fetus is all right, obtruding metal into the fetus is all right, and interfering with God's process in the womb is all right. Thus keeping a body alive six months in a hospital is all right, even though the EKG is completely flat. Indeed, God knows why one would suggest that it is immoral to preserve life but moral to preserve merely its quantity.

Father Drinan brushes that off by saying that is mere pragmatism. But all that he is really saying is that it is not good Catholic thought—which is his prerogative completely, but it does not really answer the issue.

DR. CANTRELL: It is rather well known that lawyers and physicians have difficulty enough communicating with one another, and lawyers and psychiatrists have just a terrible time of it. Here I am going to have to follow two lawyers, and it seems quite unfair. I must say that the arguments presented in the paper given by Father Drinan are quite well reasoned and I cannot find any significant basis for objecting to the statements he has given.

Dean Neibel just stole from me the point about this differentiation between the quality and the quantity of life. Unfortunately, that question, once raised, only opens the door to more profound questions that I shudder to contemplate. In fact, in this whole area of whether or not abortion is justifiable at all, the physician finds himself in a terrible dilemma. This is true even with respect to the question of life itself.

We have no high order of certainty regarding our predictions as to when the life of the mother is indeed threatened unless the fetal life is terminated. Certainly when you get into life itself the feeling of certainty fails us, particularly in my field of psychiatry. As Father Drinan pointed out so well, the prognostication of exactness is certainly impossible. We are very much aware of this.

With judgments one might make regarding the life and health of the mother, granting that these judgments might fall within the competence of the physician, one moves into an area involving things having to do with the convenience of the mother and father. In these areas the physician is treading on very dangerous territory when he permits himself to be drawn into performing an abortion. It seems to me that a physician who allows himself to be drawn into such an act, where the issue at stake is not the life or health of the mother, has reduced himself to a mere technician and has therefore ceased to be a physician in any meaningful sense. I feel the medical profession must maintain its role of the physician, and not play the part merely of a technician who fulfills the requests being made by people.

Beyond this, one cannot avoid going into the basic moral question: By what right does any human being, in the first place, interfere in the life of another human being? And, to turn it around, by what right does one human being demand that a fellow human being use his skill to interfere in the life of another? I am inquiring into a concern that is in transition. Certainly I have no answer. But I would shudder to think that physicians would be left to struggle with the problem alone, because I feel that we, as physicians have no claim to be competent to take on this monumental task. It extends far beyond the competence of the physician as such and would require the sincere support of many other individuals or of society to help us even pursue the many implications.

I have just a few questions of Father Drinan. I was a little concerned about a disparity in his presentation. He spoke of the law withdrawing, and then he spoke of mandatory counseling for the mother, and of the father being in on the decision. I find it difficult to understand how the law can withdraw on the one hand, and then make regulations on the other.

Another question I ask only half seriously: Regarding the majesty of the law and what happens to it when it is undermined by noncompliance, I wonder if Father Drinan or Dean Neibel, either one, could cite an instance where to their knowledge the law has ever withdrawn from an area it had once entered. I am a little concerned about the law withdrawing from an area once it has stated a position.

DR. RAMSEY: I would much prefer to discuss the morality rather than the legalities of abortion, but just to show you what I might do if I had a mind to, I will discuss the legalities—if I can stay on that subject.

Father Drinan's basic proposal is that the law withdraw and absent itself from the realm of abortion, that it be neutral in the matter, that it make no judgment in the legal order because such a judgment would inevitably be but a judgment about the morality or immorality of the findings. Now for those of us in the audience who believe that human life is more negotiable in human calculus than Father Drinan believes, I think we should examine most seriously that proposal.

Father Drinan's view is, in my opinion, I regret to say, a brilliant tour de force. Brilliant, but a tour de force nonetheless. It is, of course, possible for the law to withdraw from many things, such as some forms of law. The law need not be identified with taxes on alcohol; the law need not attempt to punish fornication and adultery. The Roman Catholic, be he lawyer, judge, or official of the Commonwealth of Massachusetts or some other commonwealth, can in good conscience divorce people by the dozens. He is doing something in the state, something which, as a man and a Catholic, he believes accomplishes nothing at all inasmuch as marriage is not dissolved by any power in heaven or on earth.

But why suggest that the law withdraw from the fundamental thing which is its legal glory to enforce, namely, the right to life? This is a proposal which would be utterly without foundation.

To preface my objection, and as a question to you, Father Drinan, you say in this paper that the ACLU proposes that for the first time in American jurisprudence the law "chicken out" so far as protection of the life and the right to life of the unborn child is concerned; that its proposal would recommend for the first time in American jurisprudence that the law give over to private individuals and/or the medical profession the decision as to who shall live and who shall die; and that the choice of which life shall be permitted to begin would presumably be made, not on the basis of any offense that may have been committed, but only because that life's mere existence is inconvenient to others.

I must express a different objection to the ACLU proposal by saying that it has long-range consequence for our fundamental jurisprudence in the world. For it would insert into Anglo-American law for the first time in its history the justification of the destruction of life, not in order to save another life but in order to enhance and preserve the health and greatest happiness of another person. I strongly object to the desirability of the ultimate proposal that the law try to be neutral about the most fundamental right which the law cannot be neutral about, the right to life. This would be to assign to the medical profession the decision as to whether a particular life is to be eliminated, not in order to preserve life but simply to enhance the health or greatest happiness of another human being.

At no time and under no circumstances has Anglo-American law ever sanctioned the destruction of one human being, however insignificant or useless that life may appear to be, just to increase the happiness or comfort or convenience of other individuals. Here I raise the profound moral and legal objection against the proposal with respect to the fundamental right of life. In no way could it be a desirable thing to insert into Anglo-American jurisprudence that this decision be given over to the private individual or a private profession.

So I do not think, as ecumenical as it may now be to think it, that the legislator or public can avoid some solid thinking about what is going to be decided in the matter of the definition of the right to life. I do not think that anyone sitting here can avoid thinking of himself as a citizen-magistrate and legislator. A decision must be made on the question of when is there a human life, a congener with us who is equal with us before the legal and moral order.

Now, there are various possibilities, but if there is such a thing as justifiable abortion in the legal and moral order, it will depend on some credible answer to the question: When can we put prehuman matter into the balance? When can we put a human being into the balance? Rapidly, there are several possibilities that come to mind. We can draw the line where we say we have a fellow congener, equal with every other congener before this protection of life.

You can begin, if you wish, with graduation from Rice University or from Princeton; then, at least, the person comes into rational exercise of his humanity. Going backward, you can say that it happens the day the child entered kindergarten; that is a very exciting day. But it would be more credible to say that at about age one the human being becomes a subject worthy of the protection of law. This is perhaps the age of entering into human communication, which is the great glory of man. You can go further back, of course, and say that birth is the moment, but the more I think of the order, the more I believe that the place to draw the line is at age one. Age one is better than birth as the place where we may say we have a fellow human being on the scene deserving of the protections of morality and of law. Or you can go back to viability. Even Father Drinan must resort to the moveable line in the course of absenting the law from this protection of the right to life, liberty, and the pursuit of human happiness. Then too, there is the point where the electroencephalogram can detect the fetal brain wave—not yet viability, but the brain is active. The electroencephalogram tells us something about when death is coming; can it not tell us also when a human life is beginning to arrive on the scene? Or you can go back and say, no, it is the time of quickening. Or, before that, it could be the point at which it is irrevocably settled whether it will be two or one, an identical twin or not; that is, about six or seven days after impregnation. Or you can go all the way back to impregnation. I do not see how we can answer these questions without arriving at some principle we are willing to stick to for determining when there is a fellow congener on the scene.

I oppose the adoption of the American Law Reform Bill. I do not believe we will find the answer in legislation. The morning-after pill is going to be here within a year. That should be sufficient, if we have any intelligence at all, to take care of rape cases.

The psychological ramifications have been mentioned to you. Johns Hopkins, I understand, performs one-eighth of all the abortions in the United States performed on psychological grounds. Now, I cannot believe that going through PTA for the fourth time is that much more traumatic in Baltimore than it is anywhere else in the country.

With respect to quantity and quality of life, the question arises as to whether or not the unborn child of the mother who has German measles or who took thalidomide has been damaged. It would have been far more rational, had we had the respect for life, for them all to be brought to birth and the deformed ones then removed in order to improve the quality of existence. I do not think you can find a woman who had German measles during pregnancy, and who sought and gained an abortion, who was subsequently told that her child was normal. If I were the doctor, I would not tell her anything else—meaning that if I began in untruth I would conclude in untruth, because statistics tell you nothing about the individual. You lose your shirt in Las Vegas if you count on the probabilities or possibilities having nothing to do with the individual case; yet we act as if this is a more rational thing than is the improvement of the quality of the race. Those brought up in our new generation perhaps believe infanticide would be preferable in these very distressing cases.

It is for these reasons, I believe, that Father Drinan, in his rather brilliant tour de force, suggests that before we get that pedagogy in the law it would be far better to absent the law from this area altogether.

FATHER DRINAN: Let me speak, if I may, to the quality and quantity of life. I try not to smuggle in the major premises of Catholicism, but we are all what we are.

We have always contended that parents should be responsible and bring into the world only the children that they can educate and care for. So my premise was not that mere quantity is the very desirous thing. This is certainly not my conscious thinking and not a premise, in any sense, of Catholic theology. I do not think that birth control is the issue right now.

And I don't see where fetology is contraband. It seems to me that fetology is just a carry-over of regular medicine and surgical procedure. We are not in any sense invading the womb. We are trying to help this fetus and it is just surgical technique in that regard.

Dr. Cantrell was very perceptive and saw that I was slipping in some unconscious qualifications. He asked if there is a contradiction in the withdrawal of the law, if the law were to provide for compulsory counseling and the consent of the father. Perhaps there is; I don't know. But can we leave this also to the medical profession? Doctors sometimes do not have time or the qualifications to give counseling to women who are making this decision.

With regard to the right of fathers, there is a very interesting case in California of a couple who separated. She went to a doctor seeking an abortion. When the husband heard of it, he went to the courts to seek an injunction. It was admittedly his child and he made plea before the court quite eloquently, insisting that she be forbidden to have an abortion because he would not give his consent. The injunction was denied. On appeal, the Supreme Court of California, by a divided court and without a written opinion, ruled to sustain the denial. Unfortunately for case law, the woman then decided not to have an abortion at all. I think it is justice not to permit the woman to have an abortion unless the father consents.

The question has been raised as to whether the law has ever withdrawn from an area of this kind. I think that the thrust of the law today is not to treat alcoholics or drug addicts as criminals, but rather to help them. Alcoholics need help and treatment rather than a month in jail to dry out. That just aggravates the situation. Similarly with prostitutes and drug addicts. As to homosexuality, English law now says that such conduct between consenting adults is not a crime. Likewise, fornication and adultery are crimes; the statutes in some states, moreover, set forth that it is a crime to engage in lewd and lascivious cohabitation with a person not your spouse. (How it can be lewd and not lascivious is beyond me.) Perhaps these laws are not tenable or enforceable, and that is good evidence that the law could not withdraw.

Dr. Ramsey has made an eloquent presentation of a position, namely, that the law should remain as it is now. I wish I had the eloquence that he has to argue for either the first or third option. He and I are in total agreement that the second is not a wise choice. I agree with Dr. Ramsey that logically infanticide would be more justifiable than abortion; but as a Christian lawyer I am trying to find what is best for the common good, and I propose the third option. If the law has to change in some way, then the absence of a criminal law against abortion is possibly less unsatisfactory than any other legal arrangement.

4. The Ethics of Genetic Control

The problem of genetic manipulation, though still theoretical and lacking the clinical-ethical dimension of the other problems discussed, carries a great urgency. This was apparent when it was brought forcefully to the attention of the conference by Dr. Paul Ramsey.

Recent experiments in England and the United States have confirmed the theory that a full organism can be generated from a single healthy cell. If all of the chromosome information in a given cell can be decoded and realized, a completely new organism can be formed. In theory, a carrot can be generated from a single cell of a carrot, or a frog from a frog cell. The implications are far reaching: Shall we breed a master race? Shall we breed out undesirable traits such as diabetes, baldness, and so forth? As Margaret Mead asked, "How many Churchills do we want?" All of these issues are involved in the question raised next for the conference: "Shall we clone a man?"

Paul Ramsey, a teacher and scholar in the field of Christian ethics and social theory, has produced some of the most thoughtful recent research in the social-ethical issues of our time.[1] *He is presently doing research in the field of medicine and ethics as Professor of Religion at Princeton University and Joseph P. Kennedy Research Professor of Genetic Ethics in the Department of Obstetrics and Gynecology at Georgetown University School of Medicine.*

A provocative discussion followed Dr. Ramsey's presentation, which has been amplified for publication. Included here are excerpts from the reaction of Dr. Philip Snider, distinguished geneticist at the University of Houston.

[1] Some of his thought-provoking titles are listed in the Bibliography.

Shall We Clone a Man?

Paul Ramsey

This little pig built a spaceship,
This little pig paid the bill;
This little pig made isotopes,
This little pig ate a pill;
This little pig did nothing at all,
But he's just a little pig still.[2]

The remarkable advances in biochemistry and molecular biology in recent decades, and man's increasing skill in identifying hereditary diseases or defects, seem to hold out the prospect that in the future we may be able to inaugurate a program of positive eugenic improvement through the alteration of genes. The procedure has been referred to by various names: "genetic engineering," "genetic surgery," and "genetic alchemy."

Our modern scientific knowledge and the technical possibilities it affords seem also to have breathed new life into the idea that eugenic development and man's control of his evolutionary future may be based on some form of somatic selection. Earlier proposals for eugenic reconstruction and control based on somatic selection (selection of the phenotypes to be favored in human reproduction) could appeal only to tyrants, or to invincibly technocratic minds who would have us adopt the procedures of animal husbandry.

It may be granted that in the case of some of the serious genetic defects that are *dominantly* transmitted, the birth of individuals having this same defect might in the future be prevented or decreased in incidence at comparatively small cost by having the number of carriers and sufferers to be declared genetically dead. But in the case of serious genetic diseases that are *recessively* transmitted, no significant reduction in incidence in the population could be accomplished without decreeing the genetic death of vast num-

[2] Frederick Winsor, *The Space Child's Mother Goose* (New York: Simon and Schuster, 1958).

bers of people. To attain the goals merely of preventive eugenics the gene pool would have to be forced through a very narrow corridor of those allowed to reproduce; for the more we learn about more of these diseases and their patterns of inheritance, the more radical the selection would need to be. But then add to this the goal of reconstructing mankind by the selection of superior types to be favored in reproduction, and relentlessly, again and again, the gene pool would have to be forced through even narrower corridors of those types chosen to be the sponsors and progenitors of the future generations of men.

Apart from the difficulty of knowing who is the "good" or "qualified" man, or which genetic strengths are to be favored, and apart from the difficulty of knowing who is going to decide such questions, this would be an unconscionable procedure. In the language of ethics, even if somatic or phenotypical selection could be known to be a *good* thing to do (because of its consequences for future individuals and for the species), it would not be *right* (because of its massive assaults upon human freedom and its grave violation of the respect due to men and women now alive). In face of this dilemma, genetic "alchemy" (or "engineering" or "surgery") holds out the possibility that in the future, by altering our genes before they produce future genotypes, there may be a practice of genetic medicine (at least preventively) that will both be *good* for our progeny and also *rightfully* performed upon living men and women.

Some geneticists, regarding this as a remote prospect or at least one that need not be waited for, have advocated—or suggested or pondered—schemes for the control and management of mankind's genetic future that can be described as involving a "mix" of certain techniques from present-day molecular biology, biochemistry, and genetics with some of the older notions of selecting phenotypes to be favored in human reproduction. There are two such combination proposals.

The late H. J. Muller was a passionate advocate of a program of positive genetic improvement through *voluntary* somatic selection which would be made possible today by eugenically motivated artificial insemination, frozen semen banks, and a continuing evaluation of and publicity concerning the donors available to the choice of recipients who wish to be genetic pioneers rather than simply passing on their own inherited genes. I have had occasion elsewhere to comment at length upon Muller's proposals.[3]

On this occasion I wish to bring under serious scrutiny the suggestions and predictions that Joshua Lederberg, professor of genetics and biology at Stanford University, has made in some of his recent articles and columns, above all his proposal that clonal reproduction may be a choiceworthy diversion to be introduced into human evolution, and a good way for man to control and direct the future of his species. Lederberg's notions combine somatic, psychosociological, and genetic criteria for the selection of the phenotypes to be perpetuated in reproduction with a more exquisite arsenal of techniques than H. J. Muller was able to draw from among the possible future applications of molecular biology. Lederberg seems driven to his proposals not only because, like Muller, he believes genetic surgery or alchemy to be a remote possibility, but also by the fact that after genetic reconstruction or repair has been accomplished it would then take twenty years to test whether the experiment had succeeded in producing a superior or even an adequate phenotype. Therefore he, like Muller, believes we should begin with the existing types whose strengths we know, and find a way to insure their replication in greater numbers. Since the procedures he envisions using in the control of man's future seem as remote—or as imminent in this age of galloping scientific and technological progress—as genetic engineering, Lederberg's crucial argument for clonal reproduction must be that it would replicate already existing men whose stature can now be measured and esteemed.

Shall We Clone a Man?

It is difficult to tell whether Lederberg actually advocates the prospect which he has commented on in several recent articles.[4]

[3] See Paul Ramsey, "The Moral and Religious Implications of Genetic Control," in John D. Roslansky, ed., *Genetics and the Future of Man* (New York: Appleton-Century-Crofts, 1966), pp. 109-69.

[4] See Joshua Lederberg, "Experimental Genetics and Human Evolution," *American Naturalist* 100, no. 915 (September-October 1966): 519-31; revised slightly and reprinted in the *Bulletin of the Atomic Scientists,* October 1966, pp. 4-11. Also see Lederberg's column, "Unpredictable Variety Still Rules Human Reproduction," *Washington Post,* 30 September 1967.

He seems to disavow this when he concludes by saying that "these are not the most congenial subjects for friendly conversation, especially if the conversants mistake comment for advocacy."[5] He seems to be pondering possibilities that would be worth doing if only there were some good reason for doing them, and he expressly claims only that "it is an interesting exercise in social science fiction [later: a "fantasy"] to contemplate the changes in human affairs that might come about from the generation of a few identical twins of existing personalities."[6] Still, in certain philosophies of the unavoidability of scientific and technological progress, whatever *can* be done undoubtedly *will* be done. To predict and even to ponder the prospects, while leaving open the question whether the experiment *should* be tried, or to have only relativistic ways of answering that question, amounts to much the same thing as espousal. A determinism in regard to the increasing application of medical technology combined with a radical voluntarism in regard to man's control of the future of his own species tends to erase the distinction between predictive comment and advocacy. Even if this is not a fair representation of Lederberg's position, there is ample espousal interspersed with his comment on the future possible uses of clonal reproduction.

"Clone" is a botanical term meaning "cutting"; the word "colony" is one of its cognates. Clonal reproduction means vegetative or asexual reproduction. Not all reproduction of vegetative forms is, of course, asexual or by cuttings or dispersal from a single source; but there are natural clones in plant life that seem to have advantages under certain luxuriant environmental conditions. Examples of clonal or asexual biological reproduction are the growth of an intact worm from each of the segments when an earthworm is cut in two; and the growth of identical twins from the segmentation of a single genotype in man.

Clones can be artificially created. This is the way chrysanthemums are reproduced commercially. In 1952 Drs. Robert Briggs and Thomas J. King at the Institute for Cancer Research in Philadelphia replaced the nuclei of freshly fertilized egg cells of the leopard frog

[5] This and subsequent quotations, unless otherwise noted, are from the *Bulletin of the Atomic Scientists'* version of Lederberg's article "Experimental Genetics and Human Evolution."

[6] *Washington Post,* 30 September 1967.

Rana pipiens with nuclei from blastula cells (i.e., early embryonic tissue at the end of the cleavage stage of the development of a single individual of that species). They produced a clone of free-swimming embryos (tadpoles) having the same genetic endowments as the tissue cell donor.[7] Embryonic clones were produced in 1956 using embryonic tissue older than the blastula stage.[8] The objective of the experiments was to show the stability of the nuclear transplant and the hereditability of characteristics in cell development for possible use of this knowledge in the study of cancer in various tissues. Even so, a few of the individual cloned tadpoles were allowed to grow to maturity between 1952 and 1956. Since *Rana pipiens* takes three years from egg to egg, and would require both frog and experimenter to hibernate, interest in cloning adult individuals could proceed only by shifting to a species that has a shorter generation span and other characteristics that flourish under laboratory conditions. Thus in 1961 Dr. J. B. Gurdon, zoologist at Oxford, produced a clutch of toads from the South African clawed toad *Xenopus laevis* having exactly the same genetic characteristics with each other and with the cell-donor animal—in fact a clone.

Although such an experiment has not yet been reported as successful with regard to even the laboratory mouse, the possibility that "in a few years" it can be performed upon man is nonetheless the basis for the proposal which Lederberg contemplates applying in the artful management of human reproduction. At the moment, therefore, as we examine this possible diversion or improving mechanism to be introduced into human evolution, one can have in mind (*de gustibus*) clones in vegetable life, indentical-twinning oneself, earthworms from cuttings, toads, or chrysanthemums. Dr. James F. Bonner of the California Institute of Technology believes that within fifteen years we will know how "to order up carbon copies of people"; he also speaks of this as "human mass production."[9]

---

[7] This remarkable experiment is described in Robert Briggs and Thomas J. King, "Transplantation of Living Nuclei and Blastula Cells into Enucleated Frogs' Eggs," *Proceedings of the National Academy of Sciences* 38, no. 5 (May 1952): 455-63.

[8] Thomas J. King and Robert Briggs, "Serial Transplantation of Embryonic Nuclei," *Cold Spring Harbor Symposia on Quantitative Biology* 21 (1956): 271-90.

[9] *Evening Bulletin* (Philadelphia), 23 February 1968.

Instead of clonal or vegetative reproduction, it would be more exact to call this reproduction by enucleating and renucleating an egg cell that has already been launched into life by ordinary bisexual reproduction. The question, "Shall we clone a man?" means, shall we renucleate the human fertilized egg cell?

This Drs. Robert Briggs and Thomas J. King did fifteen years ago on frogs when they showed that it was possible by some deft microsurgery upon *Rana pipiens* to replace the nucleus of a fertilized egg with a nucleus taken from a tissue cell of another frog. The cell containing the genotype of the developing embryo which resulted from the normal chance combination of parental genes was "renucleated," that is, its nucleus was replaced by one having the genotype of a single already existing individual of the species. The new frog made by "nuclear transplantation" would have been the identical twin—a generation late—of but a single "parent." This was the fundamental experiment upon which Dr. Gurdon was later to build in actually producing a clutch or clone of toads.

The fact of genetics upon which the possibility of clonal human reproduction can be envisioned is, of course, the fact that we have our genotype not only in our egg or sperm cells, but also in every cell tissue of our bodies. In this connection there are two main technical difficulties that had to be overcome in toads, and would have to be overcome in other laboratory animals and then in man.

1) We have our genotypes or genetic information in different developmental "fixes" in the various tissues and organs of our bodies. We would not grow into whole, organically differentiated bodies unless the genes for eye color were somehow "switched off" in the nuclei of the cells of our finger nails, and the genes for our finger nail characteristics were somehow "switched off" in the nuclei of cells in the eye. The switching off may be the work of special proteins called histones. These must somehow be counteracted. The trick will be to discover how to decouple these switches, so that we can begin with a nucleus and genotype taken from specialized tissue cells and enable them when transplanted to develop into a whole, organically differentiated member of the species. Alternatively, we might need to locate some special human tissue in which the cells have not become fully differentiated or specialized and therefore contain a greater degree of the totipotency of the original egg nucleus. Nuclei from early embryonic (blastula and early gas-

trula) cells in several species of amphibia have been shown to be totipotent. Dr. King reports that in *Rana pipiens* it is now well established "that blastula and early gastrula nuclei, capable of promoting completely normal development, are undifferentiated and as such are equivalent to the zygote nucleus at the beginning of development." Following the gastrula stage, at least in *Rana pipiens*, there appears to be a progressive restriction in the ability of cell nuclei to promote normal development. Dr. King writes that "the evidence at hand indicates that . . . chromosome abnormalities are not the result of technical damage sustained during the transfer procedures, but rather represent a genuine restriction in the capacity of somatic nuclei from advanced cell types to function normally following transfer into egg cytoplasm."[10] This restriction seems to be either not the case or not so extensive in the toad species *Xenopus*, and Dr. Gurdon succeeded in producing adult toads when the new nucleus was taken from gut tissue at the late tadpole stage.

2) The second formidable technical difficulty arises from interaction between the transplanted nucleus and the cytoplasm into which it is inserted. There may be a number of reasons for nuclear-cytoplasmic incompatibility leading to abnormalities in development. If, for example, "the majority of donor nuclei were in a prolonged interphase condition, there would be an ever-decreasing probability of finding in a random sample of cells nuclei that are ready to enter normally into the cleavage cycle of the egg."[11] The egg cell might cleave, causing disruption in the nucleus, and serious abnormality in development.

These are some of the problems that will have to be solved before man can give himself the choice of embarking upon clonal reproduction. Their solutions may require the combination of eggs renucleated from several different specialized human tissues in order to restore "the full range of developmental capability" there was in one's own original genotype, and to transmit this to another human being without availing oneself of the hoary old method of sexual reproduction. Yet Dr. Lederberg does not doubt that this will be accomplished, and within the time span of a few years.

[10] Thomas J. King, "Nuclear Transplantation in Amphibia," *Methods in Cell Biology* (New York: Academic Press, Inc., 1966), vol. 2, chap. 1.

[11] Marie A. Di Berardino and Thomas J. King, "Development and Cellular Differentiation of Neural Nuclear-Transplants of Known Karyotype," in *Developmental Biology* 15, no. 2 (February 1967): 123.

Reasons Said to Favor Clonality

What good reasons are there for man's adoption of clonal or vegetative reproduction when it becomes feasible? Why should we clone a man—or colonies of such men? Lederberg offers a number of reasons, both individual and social, why this might not be a bad idea.

1) "Unlike other techniques of biological engineering there might be little delay between demonstration and use. . . . If a superior individual—and presumably, then, genotype—is identified, why not copy it directly, rather than suffer all the risks . . . involved in the disruptions of recombination [?]" In this rhetorical question, Lederberg prosecutes his case for the comparative advantage of clonal reproduction over "genetic engineering." In so doing he stresses the hazards of making mistakes in reconstructing the genes and forgets for the moment the hazards (which he himself later stresses) in cloning a man or large parts of mankind. "What to do with the mishaps," he writes, "needs to be answered before we can undertake these risks in the fabrication of humans"—that is, before implanting "a special nucleotide sequence into a chromosome." Our genetic system is so complex that experiments in the surgical repair of the system are "bound to fail a large part of the time, and possibly with disastrous consequences if we slip even a single nucleotide."

Yet it is evident that Lederberg is not deterred from experimentation by mishaps, or by the question of what to do with them. What he refuses to endorse is simply waiting twenty years "to prove that the developmental perturbation was the intended, or in any way a desirable one." The "inherent complexity of the system" does not exclude experimentation—and many a mishap—on the way to clonal reproduction as the developmental perturbation and diversion to be introduced in the control and redirection of the future of the species. What is excluded is simply "any *merely prospective* experiment in algeny [genetic alchemy]" (italics added).

In other words Lederberg's premise at this point is simply expounded in the question (which, if it be an argument, is a circular one): "If a superior individual—and presumably, then, genotype—is identified, why not copy it directly, rather than suffer all the risks . . . involved in the disruptions of recombination [?]" I say circular, because the risks may be sufficient or of *such a kind* as to rebut both sorts of experimentation upon human generation.

2) There are acts of individual decision and grounds for them which, Lederberg believes, will be sufficient to insure clonality, at least as a minority practice, once it is feasible and "given only community acquiescence or indifference to its practice." For example, if one is the carrier of a serious recessive disease, he can twin from himself another carrier of the same serious recessive disease rather than risk having an overtly defective offspring by mixing his genes with those of his wife (who may also be a carrier). He can either make sure of an exact copy of himself or he can copy his spouse, and in either case attain "some degree of biological parenthood." "Copying one's spouse" would also be a way of predetermining that the offspring will be a boy or a girl (whichever is desired): "Nuclear transplantation is one method now verified to assure sex control, and this might be sufficient motive to assure its trial."

At this point Lederberg cannot avoid introducing a possibly dysgenic consequence of the adoption of clonal reproduction even for the foregoing individual reasons and as a minority practice—although his opening words disavow the disapproval. "Most of us pretend to abhor the narcissistic motives that would impel a clonist," he writes, but then he goes on to state the genetic truth, "He—or she—will pass just that predisposing genotype intact to the clone." From this the immediate inference is, "Wherever and for whatever motives close endogamy has prevailed before, clonism and clonishness will prevail." Clonal reproduction will make for clanishness. We shall return to this question, whether clonal reproduction would not in fact be a genetic disaster, because it would be a retrograde step from "adaptability," which is "man's unique adaptation."

3) Clonal reproduction might have considerable medical and social advantages. It would be a backup procedure for building men with interchangeable parts. Since the members of a colony would all be identical twins, this would make possible among them "the free exchange of organ transplants with no concern for graft rejection." More important would be the societal benefits. "Intimate communication" among men would be notably increased. Misunderstanding would be eased, and there would be a better social cohesion and co-operativeness among us. This expectation is based upon the observation that "monozygotic twins are notoriously sympathetic,

easily able to interpret one another's minimal gestures and brief words." We could produce pairs or teams of people for specialized work in which togetherness is a premium: astronauts, deep-sea divers, surgical groups. Clonal reproduction would afford us a solution to the "generational gap": "It would be relatively more important in the discourse between generations, where an elder would teach his infant copy."

Lederberg grants that he knows of no "objective studies" of the "economy of communication" among monozygotic twins. Nor do I. It would seem, however, that Lederberg has not had the experience of being the father of either monozygotic or heterozygotic twins. The crude evidence in human experience does not lend unequivocal support to the expectation that "intimate communication" would be increased without any increase of ambivalence and animosity in personal relations. Growing up as a twin is difficult enough anyway; one's struggle for selfhood and identity must be against the very human being for which no doubt there is also the greatest sympathy. Who then would want to be the son or daughter of his twin? To mix the parental and the twin relation might well be psychologically disastrous for the young. Or to look at it from the point of view of parents, it is an awful enough responsibility to be the parent of a son or daughter as things now are. Our children begin with a unique genetic independence of us, analogous to the personal independence that sooner or later we must grant them or have wrested from us. For us to choose to replicate ourselves in them, to make ourselves the foreknowers and creators of every one of their specific genetic predispositions, might well prove to be a psychologically and personally unendurable undertaking. For an elder to teach his "infant copy" is a repellent idea not because of the strangeness of it, but because we are altogether too familiar with the problems this would exponentially make more difficult.

4) Finally, and for the sake of completeness, it should be added that scientific interest is in itself for Lederberg a sufficient motivation for cloning a man, given community acquiescence or indifference to the project: "We would at least enjoy being able to observe the experiment of discovering whether a second Einstein would outdo the first one." But, of course, it would take more than twenty years to determine that.[12]

[12] "The dormant storage of human germ plasm as sperm will be replaced by the freezing of somatic tissues to save potential donor nuclei."

Reservations and Objections

1) Lederberg himself brings up the most serious genetic objection to switching to clonal reproduction. "Clonality as a way of life in the plant world," he writes, "is well understood as an evolutionary cul-de-sac. . . . It can be an unexcelled means of multiplying a rigidly well-adapted genotype to fill a stationary niche. So long as the environment remains static, the members of a clone might congratulate themselves that they had indeed won a short-term advantage." It is, Lederberg says, "at least debatable" whether "sufficient latent variability," now insured by human sexual reproduction, would be preserved "if the population were distributed among some millions of clones."[13]

This, therefore, is not his overall eugenic proposal; it is rather "tempered" clonality that he thinks might be desirable and workable. "Tempered clonality" would be an attempt to have the best of both worlds: asexual reproduction for uniformity, for intimate communication, and for multiplying proven excellence; sexual reproduction for heterogeneity and innovation. "A mix of sexual and clonal reproduction makes good sense for genetic design. Leave sexual reproduction for experimental purposes; when a suitable type is ascertained take care to maintain it by clonal propagation."

Horticultural practice, Lederberg writes, "verifies" that this "mix" or "tempered clonality" would be the best genetic design. Is it not also evident that to maintain the mix, to "temper" clonality so that the cul-de-sac of genetic rigidity can be avoided, will require careful and compulsory management of the two groups of people (or the two groups of reproductive events)? Some must be chosen to clone, others to engage in sexual reproduction. It may be that clonality "answers the technical specifications of the eugenicists in a way that Mendelian breeding does not" (because the latter continues to mix good with bad genes in sexual reproduction, while the former proceeds at once to replicate desired genotypes directly again and again). Still this "mix" of the best of two worlds picks up the worst of one: dictated breeding or nonbreeding patterns. This grand genetic design for avoiding the dysgenic consequences of switching altogether to clonal replication necessarily involves having managers decree the large numbers who shall reproduce sexually

[13] "[The] introverted and potentially narrow-minded advantage of a clonish group may be the chief threat to a pluralistically dedicated species."

and those who shall clone. The horticultural practice that verifies that a mix of the two makes the best genetic design also verifies that this can be instituted and maintained only by the power to decree: "Sexual Reproduction Forbidden." If this design does not exceed human wisdom, it certainly falls below the morally permissable.

It might also be asked what happens when one fine day a member of one of the clones decides (as a Dostoevsky might imagine) to stick out his tongue (or a more appropriate organ) at the whole scheme? What if he and a number of his fellow clonites find partners (in a neighboring clone having opposite sex, or in the ordinary population) who are willing to join them in setting a new fashion in reproduction (this time, the hoary old method you can read about in medical text books)? Would not all the recessive deleterious genes plus the mutations that have been going on in clones for years be suddenly dumped upon the world's population?

Perhaps this objection need not be raised; but if not, there would be another crucial objection—depending upon whether the human clonites we succeed in producing in the future are sterile or fertile in (forbidden) sexual reproduction. Although many of Dr. Gurdon's cloned toads were fertile, there was a higher proportion of sterility among them than among frogs of this species reared in the laboratory, and a still higher proportion than in a normal population of "wild type" *Xenopus laevis*.[14] So it may be that the eugenic

[14] "Particular interest attaches to the reproductive capacity of nuclear transplant frogs," writes Dr. Gurdon, "since this provides the most critical test of whether the nuclei from which they are derived are equivalent to the germ-cell nuclei in the range of differentiation that they can promote." (J. B. Gurdon, "Adult Frogs Derived from the Nuclei of Single Somatic Cells," *Developmental Biology* 4 [1962]: 256-73, at pp. 256, 261-62, 268-70.) His findings in the case of the infertile ones of his cloned frogs "are consistent with" the hypothesis that this was due to nuclear-cytoplasmic incompatibility and changes induced during the development of the donor embryo. That is, infertility may have been due to the fact that chromosome replication in the tissue-nucleus was out of phase with the cleavage of the cytoplasm. Dr. Gurdon counted as normal "only those frogs which fail to prove fertile and to give normal offspring (up to the average of the frogs raised in the laboratory) on at least three occasions." This indicates an abnormality in even the fertile ones: lower and more erratic fertility. Another abnormality (other than those leading to total infertility) was the fact that when frogs were cloned by nuclear transplantation from gut tissue (instead of earlier embryonic tissue) most of the male-producing donors gave rise only to sterile frogs. "This departure from equality in the number of female- and of male-producing donors," Dr. Gurdon comments, "suggests the possibility that

managers of the "mix" (tempered clonality) need not decree "Sexual Reproduction Forbidden" for all but only for some (possibly a good majority) of the clonites. Perhaps, instead, a somewhat larger proportion of the population of clonites than in the case of the ordinary "wild type" human population will be sterile. In their case, there need be no fear of dysgenic consequences if clones begin once again to engage in sexual reproduction. But then we have come upon a point which Dr. Lederberg neglects to mention: To step upon this tract may be irreversible from the first clone onward for a large minority; having once adopted vegetative reproduction, no other method of reproduction may even be possible for a significant proportion of the preferred types.

2) What shall be done with the mishaps? Dr. Lederberg concedes that "even when nuclear transplantation has succeeded in the mouse, there would remain formidable restraints on the way to human application, and one might even doubt the further investment of experimental effort." He has in mind technical difficulties, which to the layman seem about as formidable as those confronting future possible applications of genetic surgery. At the same time, Dr. Lederberg comes to the question on which he says he and his colleagues differ widely, namely, whether "anyone could conscientiously risk the crucial experiment, the first attempt to clone a man." Again, to the layman, this moral question seems as formidable for cloning a man as the "disastrous consequences if we slip even a single nucleotide" to which Lederberg appealed in opposing genetic engineering as the first choice procedure.

Dr. King was careful to explain that in the experiments performed by himself and his colleague Dr. Briggs, in which frog egg cells were successfully renucleated, the nuclei were from cells taken from embryonic tissue, not from (in every sense of the word) embryonic cells. The nuclei were from a population of cells, and cells in a population or in a tissue may not all have the same degree

endoderm nuclei from advanced donor stages are unable to give rise to normal male differentiation, so that sex reversal occurs." This is enough to indicate again the formidable technical difficulties in replicating a normal individual of any species. It is also enough to show the formidable moral question concerning the mishaps that will result from ever attempting to do this experiment on man. (See also J. B. Gurdon, T. R. Elsdale, and M. Fischberg, "Sexually Mature Individuals of *Xenopus laevis* from the transplantation of Single Somatic Nuclei," *Nature* 182: 64-65.)

of development. No doubt these were at least morphologically differentiated tissue cells (differentiated in appearance, having a ciliated brush border), but chemically the cells used may not yet have been fully differentiated embryonic cells. Thus they may have been more potent cells, not yet fully specialized, with only some of the potentialities that were in the original genotype yet switched off on the way to becoming embryonic tissue cells.[15] However, Dr. Gurdon's success in growing individual frogs from renucleated egg cells seems clearly to have been from differentiated tissue cells, not from indeterminate cells in a population.[16] It is notable, however, that he began with tissue cells from the intestines in the tadpole stage. Not just any tissue cells, or at any stage of the individual's development, would have worked. These considerations are sufficient to indicate the technical difficulties in the way of successfully cloning laboratory mice, other animals, and finally man—which make even Lederberg grant that "one may doubt the further investment of experimental effort."

The formidable moral question concerning "the crucial experiment, the first attempt to clone a man" can also be made clear from these earlier experiments. Much depended upon whether the experimenter happened to get the nucleus from a tissue cell (whether intestinal or one of a population that is still totipotent) at just the right moment in its development for placing it in the fertilized egg cell. As I understand it, if the nucleus from the donor tissue cell is in a prolonged interphase condition while the egg cell into which it is inserted is undergoing cleavage (nuclear-cytoplasmic incompatibility),[17] the result could be a monstrosity rather than normal embryonic development (King-Briggs) or an individual frog with the full characteristics of others of the species (Gurdon). Reproduc-

[15] The normal embryos obtained by King-Briggs could be explained in two different ways, as Dr. King himself pointed out: "Normal embryos obtained from transplanted nuclei can be explained equally well by assuming that a limited number of nuclei in a given cell population are totipotent, or that some nuclear changes that do occur can be reversed as a consequence of replicating in the cytoplasm of test eggs." (Marie A. Di Berardino and Thomas J. King, *op. cit.*, p. 125.)

[16] J. B. Gurdon, "The Developmental Capacity of Nuclei Taken From Intestinal Epithelium Cells of Feeding Tadpoles," *Journal of Embryology and Experimental Morphology* 10, 4 (December 1962): 622-40.

[17] See note 11 and the related text above.

ing a man by clonal replication would thus seem to be confronted with essentially the same sort of hazard, and the same formidable moral objection, as slipping a single nucleotide while repairing or reconstructing genes.

Lederberg supposes that the first crucial attempt to clone a man may be postponed "until gestation can be monitored closely to be sure the fetus meets expectations"—or until "extracorporeal gestation" permitting the same surveillance is perfected in laboratories. This obviously connects the question of what to do with the mishaps in the attempt to clone a man with the question of whether we are going to make nascent human lives *in utero* or in laboratory conditions simulating these conditions—as well as the natural or artificially induced mishaps of such undertakings—the objects of scientific experimentation. In any case, the moral question turns largely upon how we are going to "make sure the fetus meets expectations," and by what standards of judgment, warrants, or ethical points of reference.

Before asking whether Lederberg has any very good answer to that question, it should be pointed out that, while waiting to see whether anybody is going to venture to clone himself or another congener, a diversion on the way to human clonality will continue to reduce the difference between what is now being done with animal egg cells in laboratory cultures and the future possible event of cloning a man. "Human nuclei, or individual chromosomes and genes, will be recombined with those of other animal species; these experiments are now well under way in cell culture. Before long we are bound to hear of tests of the effect of dosage of the human twenty-first chromosome on the development of the brain of the mouse or the gorilla." Somewhat triumphantly Lederberg adds, "The mingling of individual human chromosomes with those of other mammals assures a gradualistic enlargement of the field and lowers the threshold of optimism or arrogance, particularly if cloning in other mammals gives incompletely predictable results."

This brings us again to the same formidable moral objection. In the case of cloning a man, the question is what to do with mishaps, whether discovered in the course of extracorporeal gestation in the laboratory or by monitored uterine gestation. In case a monstrosity, a subhuman or parahuman individual results, shall the experiment simply be stopped and this artfully created human life killed? In mingling individual human chromosomes with those of the "higher" mammals (given sufficient dosage and "a few years") what shall be done if the resulting individual lives seem remarkably human? Moreover, Lederberg not only contemplates experiments "augmenting" animal cell cultures with "fragments of the human chromosome set," but the reverse is also to be done: "Clonal reproduction, and *introduction of genetic material from other spheres*" are two paths already opened up in *human* evolution (italics added). Lederberg "infers" these twin genetic policies instead of taking the other and somewhat longer road to genetic engineering. But these are surely paths no less fraught with mishaps knowingly if not intentionally created. We must face the grave moral question of what to do with them.

On this fundamental question it must simply be said that Lederberg is not very helpful. He calls for reasoned and sensitive moral judgment on these matters but fears that the issue will be settled adversely if the public gets wind of what is now or (he believes) shortly will be going on in laboratories, or on the basis of publicity concerning the first results of cloning a man or giving the human chromosome set large dosages from "other spheres." "The precedents affecting the long-term rationale of social policy will be set," he concludes, "not on the basis of well-debated principles, but on the accident of the first advertised examples. The accidents might be as capricious as the nationality, the batting average, or the public esteem of a clonant; the handsomeness of a parahuman progeny; the private morality of the experimenters; or public awareness that man is a part of the continuum of life."

The accident of the first examples (advertised or not) and the probability of a great many of them is the question now under examination. The "accidentality" of how the question of these accidents might be settled by an unthinking public is not at issue. We may grant the nonrationality and the capriciousness of settling any human moral public policy question by any of the foregoing criteria (including the last one: the fact that man is a part of the continuum of life). However, it is just as nonrational to refer, as Lederberg does, to "the touchiness of experimentation on obviously human material." That is the issue of "subhuman" hybrids, or artifacts of applications of molecular biology, namely, whether this "touchiness" is not entirely justified, indeed prohibitive.

Lederberg begins by announcing quite correctly that "scientists are by no means the best qualified architects of social policy,"[18] and by limiting their function to the essential tasks of interpreting the technical challenges facing humanity and having the forethought to determine various scientific efforts that might be put forth to meet them. But when he comes to the questions of purpose and value that must provide the foundation of any public policy, it is still a purely scientific value that heads all the rest, a test most likely to appeal to "skeptical scientists." It is not anything morally substantive about man himself, his nature or his purpose, but "the growing richness of man's *inquiry about* nature, about himself, and his purpose" (italics added). This indeed is the arch scientific value. Despite his previous announcement, Lederberg makes this the overriding value. Interspersed with this is some truly admirable moral rhetoric about how this leads to "a humble appreciation of the value of different approaches to life and its questions, of respect for the dignity of human life, and of individuality." This is plainly the "humility" that will keep open the options and answer no moral question in the area of eugenics until the scientific accounting of our genetic options is complete. It is also one that will never find any moral limit upon the choice among options. Instead there will be only limits derived from a "rigorously mechanistic formulation" of the life sciences. This would seem to be the reason Lederberg decries "the arrogance that insists on an irrevocable answer to any of these questions of value."

On the basis of this article alone, it is evident that Lederberg has made his choice between humane civilization and a civilization

[18] In the light of this remark, it would seem that the testimony of Dr. Lederberg and his Stanford colleague, Dr. Arthur Kornberg, before the Senate Subcommittee on Government Research on the resolution of Senator Walter E. Mondale (D-Minn.) to set up a National Commission on Health, Science, and Society was less than forthright and more than disingenuous (*New York Times*, 9 March 1968). "How the human species can foresee and plan its own future is the real subject of these hearings," said Dr. Lederberg. "No subject is more important." But the issues were too important to be left with a national commission. One may indeed doubt whether a commission "charged with making substantive prescriptions, after one year's study, about the biological policy of the human species," is the answer. But who then? Both Drs. Lederberg and Kornberg abdicated giving any answer to this question. They seemed to deny that recent progress in genetics poses special moral, social, or political problems for mankind. Both called for more research and more funds for research—for a public well educated in the concepts of science and a scientific community richly supplied with data. In short, they called for a purely scientific answer to the moral questions arising from genetic and nucleic acid research, even if they did not quite claim that only scientists themselves should fashion public policy concerning these matters.

based on scientific-mechanistic values alone (if the latter is a proper manner of speaking). "Humanistic culture," he writes, "rests on a definition of man which we already know to be biologically vulnerable." This is a decision made not without trouble by Lederberg the man, since he knows that "the goals of our culture rest on a credo of the sanctity of the human individual." Despite this, however, Lederberg the scientist can only pose the question that for him has but one obvious answer: "How is it possible for man to demarcate himself from his isolated or scrambled tissues and organs on one side, and from experimental karyotypic hybrids on the other?"

This entire proposal that we should clone a man and proceed with mixing chromosomes from "other spheres" with human material is, therefore, simply an extrapolation of what we *should* do from what we *can* do. There are really only technical questions to be decided. At root, therefore, the proposal denies that the mishaps constitute a crucial moral problem. The mishaps are only misadventures that may or may not awaken in a capricious public a latent humanism sufficiently powerful to stop the experiment.

Specifically concerning the mishaps, Lederberg says only that "*pragmatically*, the *legal* privileges of humanity will remain with objects that *look* enough like men to grip their *consciences*, and *whose nurture does not cost too much*" (italics added). The reader is told later that "the handsomeness of a parahuman progeny" would be a capricious test (as indeed it is). At this point Lederberg's own latent humanism rises to the surface of his scientific pondering of the options, and he is impelled to write, "Rather than superficial appearance of face or chromosomes, a more rational criterion of human identity might be the potential for communication within the species, which is the foundation on which the unique glory of man is built." With that statement this paragraph once ended; and it seems a minimum statement of a basis for the respect and protection of human life. But the statement was promptly suppressed. In the version of his article which appeared in the *American Naturalist*, Lederberg appended a footnote in which he stated, "On further reflection I would attack any insistence on this suggestion (which I have made before) as another example of the intellectual arrogance that I decry a few sentences above—a human foible by no means egregious."[19] That judgment was made a part of the text in

[19] *Op. cit.*, p. 530, n. 2.

the revision of the article for the *Bulletin of the Atomic Scientists.* The paragraph in which was expressed the "foible" of enunciating a possibly human criterion for demarcating man from other genetic spheres or from artificially scrambled genes concluded with the statement, "Insistence on this suggestion, of course, would be an example of the intellectual arrogance decried above." In the case of the mishaps, therefore, we are left with only the pragmatic problem of agreeing upon the line to be drawn empirically between those that "look" human enough and those that "look" subhuman or parahuman. Given this, we could proceed to manufacture, select, and eliminate progeny. This is simply a way of saying that the mishaps do not constitute a moral problem, and that the management and control of human evolution and of the future generations of men has no intrinsic limits. The procedure has consequences only, and goals "read in" to the object-matter by the experimenter and our future possible public policy managers.

The same muddled moral reasoning is to be found in Lederberg's comments on the problem of abortion.[20] He rightly observes that "unless we learn to deal with this contemporary issue in a humane way, we will never in the future be able to cope with the subtler problems of qualitative intervention in the finer points of human reproduction." The same perspectives we have examined above are applied to this currently pressing issue, and the yield is no greater, for anyone moderately accustomed to the logic and problems of ethics.

Lederberg states that the question "When does life begin?" can have no answer "apart from the purposes for which the question is raised." This is a fine, formal requirement of moral discourse; and of course the purpose for which the question is raised in the matter of abortion is to determine when human life has rights in exercise and is a life due to be given respect and protection as a congener. But Lederberg proceeds to ask and answer the question with quite another purpose in mind—which is all right, but not (according to Lederberg's own formal requirement) in the present context. "Life is a continuum; if life had a beginning at all, it was an event that occurred some 3 billion years ago." Thus Lederberg gets back the

[20] "A Geneticist Looks at Contraception and Abortion," *The Changing Mores of Biomedical Research: A Colloquium on Ethical Dilemmas from Medical Advances,* held at the 48th Annual Session of the American College of Physicians, San Francisco, 12 April 1967, in *Annals of Internal Medicine* 67, no. 3, supp. 7 (September 1967): 25-27.

answer *he* prejudged, by forgetting that the question has different meanings in different contexts. This leads to irrelevancies (in the context of the purpose for which the question of abortion is raised) such as, "No more than a small percent of the total nucleotide composition of the diploid human nucleus differentiates the human being from the ape, or the monkey, or other primate species." Argument from the continuum of life (which was not in question) is sufficient to place genetic material over the 3 million years, human sperm, ovum, fetal life, and at least the newborn human being on the same level. (This is remarkably like the identification of the problem of abortion with that of contraception in some conservative Roman Catholic circles—to the conclusion that sperm and ovum, the zygote and embryo, should alike be protected from artificial assault.)

The analogy between Lederberg's remarks on abortion and his views on the "finer points" of intervention in human reproduction (in the text above) becomes most clear when he remarks—not incorrectly if communication is the test—that "an operationally useful point of divergence of the developing organism [in the whole continuum] would be at approximately the first year of life, when the human infant continues his intellectual development, proceeds to the acquisition of language, and then participates in a meaningful cognitive interaction with his mother and with the rest of society. At this point only does he enter into the cultural tradition that has been the special attribute of man by which he is set apart from the rest of the species." [Cf. above ". . . communication with the species, which is the foundation on which the unique glory of man is built."] But again Lederberg draws back from having drawn a human and a moral line: this time in regard to the treatment to be accorded the newborn; above, in regard to what we should do with clonal mishaps. "I do not advocate a discussion of infanticide," he says, having just begun such a discussion at its most essential point (if the point is ethically correct). Just as, above, he drew back to those artifacts of the proposed applications of molecular biology that/who "look" enough like men to grip our consciences (emotions?), so here he observes that "we are all so emotionally involved with infants that this in itself is enough to create an inevitable and a pragmatically useful [*sic*] dividing line [at birth]."

Lederberg has therefore provided himself with no intellectual foundation for the immediately following dictum: "To discuss the fetus during prenatal life as if he were a human being is merely to reflect the emotional involvement of that observer." Surely he had just appealed to the same sort of emotional involvement with another life during that part of the continuum from birth to age one as the only ground for not practicing infanticide. Of course, the latter emotional involvement is that of most of mankind, while the former may be "a set of tastes not shared by the majority."

Then is Lederberg recommending that moral questions and public policy be settled by polls of people's emotional involvement with prenatal life, with babies in incubators, with babies after normal birth, with experimental karyotypic hybrids? No; on a generous interpretation, none of these "sets of tastes" (and not simply the one he opposes) should "be confused with an objective biological standard by which we can set up principles of social order as criteria for the operation of law." Since, however, from this no objective ethical standards have been shown to be forthcoming, and since any insistence on the test of a potentiality for communication within the species would be an instance of "arrogance" insufficiently informed of the continuum of life, Lederberg is driven in the end to hortatory appeals: "Help put this [abortion] issue on the plane where it deserves to be discussed: What are the realistic consequences of revision of the law for human welfare in the light of your own knowledge of the continuity of biological life and evolution?" In other words, while Lederberg does not want only scientists to make public policy, he wants only a scientific judgment to be made.

In the discussion following this San Francisco colloquium, Lederberg was asked whether in the case of monstrous births he would approve of infanticide or of allowing them to die.[21] His answer combined a genuine concern for human welfare ("before I would advocate killing even monstrous births, I would want to inquire what the effect might be on the standards of care for other infants") with opting for the time of birth as the significant dividing line (we should "do as much as we can to bring about the earliest possible detection of aberrations so that these genetic deaths can be made to occur at the period where they would have the least strenuous consequences for the other members of our society"). As for aberrations that would still sometimes be born, his inclination

[21] *Ibid.*, pp. 54-55.

would be that instead of killing them or letting them die, "they may be such interesting objects for humane observation and experimentation that it may be very well worth making very great efforts to keep them alive once they have started to exist." One may ask why, on Lederberg's principles of continuity, all lives before "they have started to exist [i.e., been born]" might not be fit subjects for medical experimentation?

3) These genetic possibilities mark an extraordinary "borderline" to which human ingenuity has brought mankind in the present day. Before stepping across that borderline we should let it teach us something. The borderline, as Helmut Thielicke has written, is "the truly propitious place for acquiring knowledge"[22]—ethical knowledge. This genetic proposal, like the minority practice of artificial insemination from a nonhusband donor, is a borderline case that throws into bold relief the nature of human parenthood, which both place under assault. If cloning men had no other consequences, this alone would be sufficient to fault it. Our consideration of the proposal should enliven in our minds an important feature of parenthood which serves "to make and to keep human life human."[23] Any fundamental assault upon this feature is an assault upon the human and the personal element in parenthood.

Man is an embodied person in such a way that, in important respects, he *is* his body. He is the body of his soul no less than he is the soul (mind, will) of his body. There are more ways to violate a human being—or to engage in self-violation—than to coerce his free will or his rational consent. An individual's body, including his sexual nature, belongs to him, to his humanum, his personhood and self-identity, in such a way that the bodily life cannot be reduced to the class of the animals over which Adam was given unlimited dominion. To suppose that it can is bound to prove antihuman—sooner rather than later.

The nature of human parenthood may be summed up by saying that conjugal intercourse is a life-giving act of love-making or a

---

[22] Helmut Thielicke, *The Ethics of Sex*, trans. John W. Doberstein (New York: Harper and Row, 1964), p. 199. See also Helmut Thielicke, *Theological Ethics*, vol. 1, *Foundations* (Philadelphia: Fortress, 1966), p. 580.

[23] Paul L. Lehmann, *Ethics in a Christian Context* (New York: Harper and Row, 1963), p. 99.

love-making act of life-giving. Procreation and the communication of bodily love, nurturing and strengthening the bonds of life with life, belong indefeasibly together—not, it is true, in every act of marriage but between the two persons who are married. From their one-flesh unity together comes the one flesh of the child—not, of course, because of any materiality genetics could prove or disprove but because the communications of love and parenthood are both deeply personal acts and relations. This is all the more so because they are not done exactly rationally. More of the self is engaged because this bodily presence and these bodily events are not directed by the dominating rational will alone. Whatever substrata of uses there may be in sexual energy beyond the needs of the species, and whatever the mechanics of heredity, these are subsumed onto a human plane in conjugal love and in parenthood.

We procreate new beings like ourselves in the midst of our love for one another, and in this there is a trace of the original mystery by which God created the world because of his love. God created nothing apart from his love, and without the divine love was not anything made that was made (John 1). Neither should there be among men and women—whose man-womanhood (and not their minds or wills only) is in the image of God—any love-making set out of the context of responsibility for *pro*creation, or any begetting apart from the sphere of human love and responsiveness. As God's love binds himself to the world and the world to himself, so there is a reflection of this love in the claim God has placed upon men and women in their creation, and in the task and joy God has assigned to them when he bound procreation and the nurturing of marital love together in human sexuality. Thus is our man-womanhood created in covenant and for covenant—the covenant of marriage and the covenant of parenthood.

In their sciences, men may be able to subdue the mystery of procreation; they may be able to subdue all the wonders of human sexual response. But they cannot subdue the mystery inherent in the fact that human communications of marital love are eminently also the place where we engage as *pro*creators as we establish and step into the covenant of parenthood. Men can only deny that there is any mystery to be honored here; they can only reduce the matter to an accident of biological nature that could as well not have been so—or that can be changed to vegetative reproduction.

Herein men usurp dominion over the human as over the animals. This is bound to pierce the heart of the humanum in sex, marriage, and generation.

The "experiment" involved in the thought "shall we clone a man?" and the technical possibility of doing so on a vast scale may be the truly propitious place for acquiring the knowledge that the link between sexual love and procreation is not in us a matter of specific or animal consequences only but is of truly human and personal import. To put radically asunder what nature and nature's God joined together in parenthood when he made love procreative, to disregard the foundation of the covenant of marriage and the covenant of parenthood in the reality that makes for at least minimally loving procreation, to attempt to soar so high above an eminently human parenthood is inevitably to fall far below—into a vast technological alienation of man. Limitless dominion over procreation means the boundless servility of man-womanhood. The conquest of evolution by setting sexual love and procreation radically asunder entails depersonalization in the extreme. The entire rationalization of procreation, its replacement by replication, can only mean the abolition of man's embodied personhood.

Another thing we can learn from clonality as a thought-experiment, or as a borderline prospect, is a proper historical perspective upon the stress which earlier ages placed on procreation as the chief end of marriage. Never before in our history until now has breeding been so highly exalted as the chief end, indeed the isolated end, to be pursued by marriage as an institution or by surrogate institutions of our own devising. Never was breeding so far separated from personal, human love. Never was breeding (or replication) set so far afield from the relations in which men and women express *fides* toward one another (not even in times past when *fides* meant only something negative or remedial). This is done from one side by those of our contemporaries who would justify acts of sexual love beyond the sphere of responsible procreation (by definition, marriage—which then is more and more for the procreation and education of children only). It is done from the other side by any scheme for the entire rationalization and control of "reproduction" (itself a metaphor of a machine civilization, one that already gets rid of the persons and may, by a next step, suggest getting rid of one of the "producers" by means of clonal replication).

Underlying Premises

Up to this point we have, so to speak, been doing genetic ethics. We have been examining this specific eugenic proposal in the light of some of the moral norms that generally commend themselves to rational moral agents, or in which we may be instructed by the borderline case of clonal reproduction when this is seriously put forward as a project worthy of man. We need, finally, to stand off at a distance from these detailed incriminations or commendations of clonal reproduction in order to examine its chief philosophical underpinnings.

There is a total life view at work in the grand design of mixing clonal with sexual reproduction in the control of man's evolution. This same outlook is at work also in projects for positive or progressive eugenics and the redirection of the human future by means of the "chemical control of genotypes"—"genetic engineering." In fact it may be said that the ethical violations we have noted on the horizontal plane (coercive breeding or nonbreeding, injustice done to individuals or to mishaps, the violation of the nature of human parenthood) are a function of a more fundamental happening in the vertical dimension, namely, that of hubris and "playing God."

These, of course, are not very helpful characterizations of the attitude that is in control of some, if not all, of the progressive eugenic proposals that have been put forward in the modern age. We shall have to see if the fundamental outlook I have in mind can be analyzed somewhat more closely, and ask what then we are to think about this outlook. In undertaking to do this, I shall again make use of Lederberg's article. It would not be fair, however, to quote him on this point in such a way as to suggest that these viewpoints are in any way exclusively or especially his. They are merely symptomatic of modern thought-forms in general (including some recent religious speculations that have placed all religious impulse behind the triumphalism of secular man, none to his essential correction or to critical judgment upon our inveterate utopianism). The following citations from Lederberg are, therefore, simply prisms through which can clearly be seen the operative, but unspoken premises of modern man in general, which must be called radically into question.

1) The first of these premises is the replacement of categories appropriate to the *ethical* evaluation of behavior or of moral agency by categories appropriate to the elaboration and evaluation of *designs*. This is why we so readily speak of "replacing evolution by *art*" (italics added), and proceed on the assumption that the means that are in the offing in the "geneticist's *repertoire*" (italics added) shall come into use. This is because designs are controlled only by ends external to them. Only the self-elected purposes of engineering place any limit upon what we shall undertake to do to pliable matter, limited only by what that matter yields to our purposes.

To the contrary, in all the ages of man founded at all upon moral premises it was silently if not explicitly assumed that "making" is quite different from "doing." The exercise of reason in practical applications of "art," in making designs or in engineering consequences, is one sort of human activity. The exercise of practical reason in political and moral agency ("doing") is another. The homeland of ethics is in the latter, not in the former or in any of its analogies in the conduct of human affairs, the "management" of crises or of man's own future. Genuine moral relations and moral considerations come into view only for man the doer, not for man the maker. Instead of saying that modern man is prone to exercise an unlimited hubris or "play God" over the future, it is better to say that he thinks of himself as simply engineering the future—a humble maker artfully designing himself and his kind. From such a program ethics has already been excluded, and not only by the Dionysian types.

2) The second premise is a more paradoxical one, and at the same time more widely and profoundly symptomatic of the modern condition. This is the combination of boundless determinism with boundless freedom in all our thoughts. Mechanism and arbitrary freedom go together. This is why Lederberg can correctly write that "in the last decade, molecular biology has given us a mechanistic understanding of heredity"—with the unproved assumption that this is all there is to be said about the *destiny* that underlies and calls human freedom into play. And he continues by saying that this same molecular biology has given us "an outline of the methodology needed to do the same for development"—as if that is all that need be said about the absolute and unrestricted *freedom* with which man can now step forth to impose control over the future by

making use of the "outline" provided by our mechanistic understanding of heredity.

There is no end, no limit to the mechanism, only an immanent determinism. There is no end, no limit to human freedom, only choices immanent to freedom's own election (plus the recalcitrance, if any, to be found in the "outline" of future possibilities). Looking into an open future, Lederberg can write that we now have "the new evolutionary theory needed to fashion a self-modifying system that plans, however imperfectly, its own nature." And we have seen how extensive is the contemplated self-modification. As there is no destiny overruling man's rulings, so there are no essential limits from humanistic values not already vulnerable to biological determinism. Strangely, heredity understood mechanistically has fashioned a limitless self-fashioning system (man), however imperfect the self-making may turn out to be.

The boundless determinism and the boundless freedom contained in this thought is not solely or mainly a product of science. It is rather a widespread cultural phenomenon or thought-form characteristic of man in the modern period. Dostoevsky discerned this to be true. Where there is no God, no *destiny* moving in men and toward which men move, then self-modifying freedom must be the man-God. This is necessarily correlated with the unlimited subjugation of everything else, of human reality as it now is and of the genetic future, to the determinations of that usurped and absolute freedom.

It does not matter whether this is said with Dionysian exuberance or with the studied indifference of a scientific mind. The mind in any case floats freely over everything that is and contemplates that it may not be, or may be altogether otherwise. It thinks to create something out of nothing, or out of our chance and random chromosomes. Thus, in regard to possible reactions to the "fantasy" of switching to clonal reproduction, Lederberg observes that "if sexual reproduction were less familiar we might make the same comment about that."[24] He is "more puzzled by the rigor with which asexual reproduction has been excluded from the vertebrate as compared with the plant world" than he will be by man's achieve-

[24] *Washington Post,* 30 September 1967. The *title* of this column is also of considerable significance: "Unpredictable Variety Still Rules Human Reproduction."

ment in changing all that. What can be the explanation of this puzzling penchant for sexual reproduction? "That clonal reproduction is mainly confined to plants," Lederberg writes, "may be a mere accident of cell biology." But whether it is accident or mechanistic determination that created us this way, there is in any case no reason for man to respect and honor any feature of the creation. He is now absolutely free to change all that—to choose to become his own self-creator.

Lederberg briefly tells his own myth for this: "In mythical terms, human nature began with the eating of the fruit of the tree of knowledge." In the original myth that meant the knowledge of good and evil; for Lederberg it means the knowledge of the accidents of cell biology or of the determinism disclosed to us by molecular biology and the laws of heredity. This is the way we have come to understand the garden of life in which man's freedom is planted. The functionally correlated statement must immediately follow: "The expulsion from Eden only postponed our access to the tree of life." For primitive man, that meant a natural immortality. For Lederberg it means neither immortal nor creaturely life, but *dominion* of man, man self-determining the conditions of future human life, the terms upon which future generations of men and our species in general shall live and move and have their being. When future generations ask us, "Where were you when the foundations of our humanum were laid?" the answer to be given them is quite evident—provided one believes that human freedom should now lay hold of godhood.

We may make the claim that the philosophy (not the science) underlying all this is untrue. This may take some temerity in the present age, but it is a not unreasonable assertion. We can say that as for me and my house we will continue to practice genetic ethics and genetic counseling and the elimination of grave defects in the simple service of creaturely life. This, I say, may require some temerity, but it is not unreasonable. In any case, there is no reason for anyone to be frightened out of his wits by the relativists, subjectivists, and skeptics who in moral science have not been able to make their case. Nor should he be frightened out of his ethical wits by grand eugenic designs.

It may take some temerity to oppose these grand proposals for man's self-reconstruction and control over the evolutionary future, but this is not an unreasonable position. In the present age the attempt will be made to deprive us of our wits by comparing our current objections to schemes of progressive genetic engineering or cloning men to some earlier opposition to inoculations, blood transfusions, or the control of malaria. These things are by no means comparable: the practice of medicine in the service of life is one thing; man's unlimited self-modification of the genetic conditions of life would be quite another matter.

Nor does it suffice to say that we are already introducing vast changes in the environment, and that these environmental changes are in fact altering mankind's genetic basis. Even if it is true that "the jet airplane has already had an incalculably greater effect on human population genetics than any conceivable program of calculated eugenics would have," the argument cuts both ways. Mankind has not evidenced much wisdom in the control and redirection of his environment. It would seem unreasonable to believe that by adding to his environmental follies one or another of these grand designs for reconstructing himself, man would thereby show a sudden increase in wisdom. If genetic policy-making were not miraculously improved over public policy-making in environmental and political matters, then access to the tree of life (meaning genetic management of future generations) could cause grave damage. It could cause the genetic death God once promised, but by his mercy withheld in order that his creature, despite having sought to lay hold of godhood, might still live and perform a limited, creaturely service of life. Then boundless freedom and self-determination would in its end results become boundless destruction, even as its methods all along included the unlimited subjugation of man to his own rational designs and designers. No man or collection of men are likely to have the wisdom to rule the future in any such way.

Conclusion

Nothing said above should inhibit the use of genetic information in the practice of medicine, nor is it intended to do so. In medical practice the patient is an individual human being and his (or her) probable offspring. The patient is not "society" or the "future" or "distant generations" as such. Having rejected on moral and as well on scientific grounds some of the grand designs for treating or improving those nonpatients, it might be well in conclusion to summarize some of the things we should now be doing in actual medical practice, and in public policy related to this. From these primary concerns we ought not to be distracted by an overweening desire to master the future of our species.

There is, of course, no question about the need for more extensive genetic counseling, and for the education of people in the availability of these services. As our knowledge of inherited grave defects becomes more exact, and especially when geneticists are able to identify more of these diseases even before one instance has occurred in a family, there will be need for premarital genetic counseling. If we require premarital blood tests to protect the innocent or the unknowing from being inflicted with venereal disease, it would be entirely proper as a matter of public policy (if and when the science is exact enough) to require certain premarital genetic tests to protect the innocent and the unborn—and to protect the unknowing partners contemplating marriage from complicity in a tragic birth which they may not want and should not want.

As a matter of public policy, we could and probably should, go further. There may well be defects that are identifiable—say, in the case of grave dominantly inherited diseases—which would warrant using the marriage licensing power of the state to prevent their transmission. This would be in the service of life and in the service of the only patients known to medical practice. After all, it ought never to be believed that everyone has an unqualified right to have children, or that children are simply for one's own fruition. Instead, procreation is the service of human beings to come, and the ordinary right to have children could readily become in given instances the duty *not* to do so. Then, beyond premarital tests and counseling, it is arguable that in certain cases it would be desirable for public policy to condition and restrict marriage licenses by this present or future knowledge in genetics. This should not be taken *ab initio* to be too great an infringement of human liberty, because the freedom of parenthood is a freedom to good parentage, not a license to produce seriously defective individuals to bear their own burdens.

Anyone concerned with genetic counseling and the practice of genetic medicine in the service of life should, then, be set against all those influences in our society leading to steadily increasing illegitimacy and to the mores by which getting pregnant is fast becoming an accepted way or an "institution" for getting married. These practices are sufficient to void the individuals' voluntary genetic responsibility and the premarital tests or conditions that might be warranted in a rational use of our growing knowledge of genetics. We need to mean what we say when we speak of "responsible parenthood."

Moreover, sexual intercourse and/or marriage at an increasingly early age are known to be dysgenic. It is well known that young women, no less than women who bear children when they are past the age of thirty-five, have a greater incidence of chromosome difficulties. Studies made in Japan, where the average upper age of childbearing has rapidly gone down to thirty-five while the age when women have their first child has over recent decades gone up to twenty, have shown not only a decrease of mongolism, which rises exponentially when the woman is of older age, but also a marked decrease of congenital defects attributable to childbearing at an early age.[25]

As a final illustration, there are abundant studies which show that, in mammals other than man, sperm that after intercourse has aged more before ovulation of the egg it fertilized is apt to produce a far greater incidence of congenital malformations than sperm ejaculated closer to the time of ovulation. So there are scientists who believe that, in human beings, the practice of the rhythm method of conception control is wrong, not because it does not work but because it does. That is to say, the essence of the rhythm method is to locate sexual intercourse as far as possible from the time of ovulation. If, nevertheless, conception takes place it will be from an older sperm than might otherwise be the case, and not from a random sample of these "time-acts" of intercourse. The studies mentioned above seem to show that this is dysgenic. Some scientists, therefore, believe that the time may come when we will have enough evidence to know that we should all practice contraception for the entire time considered infertile by the rhythm calculations, and then have procreative intercourse only when the temperature chart goes up, in order to optimize the conceptus from sperm as fresh as the ovum it fertilizes. Even as the temperature chart is now used in order to enable a woman to have a child, this could be a way of enabling

[25] Ei Matsunaga, "Possible Genetic Consequences of Family Planning," a paper read before a seminar of the International Planned Parenthood Federation, Tokyo, 26 May 1966. *National Institute of Genetics,* Mishima, Yata, Japan.

women in a population to avoid a significantly greater incidence of congenital deformities.[26]

With all these "sooner anxieties" and the many things needing to be done in the application of genetics in the service of life, it would seem prodigal to devote thought, energy, and educational resources to the practice of genetics on that nonpatient: the species. It is, in general, the grand designs of positive or progressive eugenics that should be opposed in the name of the right and the good, in the name of more urgent and practical applications of genetics in medicine, and because of our lack of wisdom to create —by favoring selected phenotypes—an evidently stronger and more adaptable species than nature has achieved in man pluralistically.

But what of negative eugenics by means of introducing chemical changes in the genotype ("genetic engineering")? If in future acts of genetic surgery we stick close to assured knowledge of the gene that needs to be rendered inoperative, and do not blend this with grandiose notions of genetic improvement of the species, a preventive use of "genetic engineering" cannot be denied a possible place in medical service to patients. I have yet to discover any reason to reverse the formal judgment I made upon first venturing into this science-based moral question:

> Should the practice of such medical genetics become feasible at some time in the future it will raise no moral question at all—or at least none that are not already present in the practice of medicine generally. Morally, medical genetics to enable a man and a woman to be able to engender a child without some defective gene they have been discovered to carry would seem to be on all fours with treatment to cure infertility. . . . Any significant difference arises from

[26] There is also mounting evidence from studies of human reproduction, including evidence gathered by rhythm clinics, that among pregnancies resulting from intercourse a number of days before ovulation there are an abnormal number of males. (See R. Guerrero, "Time of Insemination in the Menstrual Cycle and Its Effect on the Sex Ratio" [Thesis, Harvard School of Public Health, Boston, Mass., January 1968].) Thus, acts of sexual intercourse *qua* procreative are a series of "time-acts," and to disturb this by a selection favoring (if only by "accidents") those days more remote from ovulation may as a consequence disrupt the proportion of males and females in the future population. If anything, the optimum good of the conceptus and the good in the nature of bisexual reproduction, marriage, and the male-female balance, would require selection in favor of intercourse at the time of ovulation. This would require the use of temperature charts, etc., *for this purpose* whenever procreation is wanted, and the use of assured methods of contraception during the remainder of the cycle.

> the vastly greater complexity of the practice of genetic surgery and the seriousness of the consequences if because of insufficient knowledge an error is made. . . . The science of genetics and medical practice based on it would be obliged to be fully informed of the facts and it should have a reasonable and well-examined expectation of doing more good than harm (to this patient, this progeny) by eliminating the genetic defect in question.[27]

Joshua Lederberg's writings have made me more aware of the danger of "slipping a single nucleotide" in genetic surgery. This danger, and the complexity of our genetic mechanism in general, may make it unlikely that we will ever know enough assuredly to control remedial medical applications of genetic surgery when this is submitted to the test of "a reasonable and well-examined expectation of doing more good than harm" to the patient to be born by eliminating the genetic defect in question. Still I see no reason for altering the ethical verdict upon this possibility.

Genetic surgery for the sake of the newborn, therefore, cannot be removed from among future possible practices of genetic medicine. In any case, applications of our genetic information in medical practice should never lose sight of the physician's real patients—the man, the woman, the child to be born—or replace them by such nonpatients as the species or our control of human evolution. If this includes preventive genetic surgery, it is because such action is required and may reasonably be done in the service of these lives.[28]

* * *

[27] Paul Ramsey, "The Moral and Religious Implications of Genetic Control," *op. cit.*, pp. 152-53.

[28] It is significant that when proponents of positive eugenic designs to be worked on the future are hard pressed, they frequently repair again to this sound limit upon the practice of medicine upon human beings. Dr. Leon R. Kass, biochemist at the National Institutes of Health, Bethesda, Maryland, responded to Lederberg's column in the *Washington Post,* 30 September 1967, in a Letter to the Editor, printed 3 November 1967. Dr. Kass pointed to the fact that scientific and technical progress has a momentum of its own which is apt to erase the distinction between "it can be done" and "it should be done" or "it has to be done." "Biologists today," he wrote, "are under strong obligation to raise just such questions publically so that we may deliberate *before* the new biomedical technology is an accomplished fact." He asked, "Is the human will sufficient authority to advocate or to attempt to clone a man?" "Should an independent scientist carry out such an experiment in the absence of public authorization?" "Who should control the genetic planning?" In the case of mishaps, "Who will or should care for 'it' and what rights will 'it' have?"

DR. SNIDER: I have a good many ideas. A limited negative eugenics certainly is well accepted now. There are numerous examples: entering into marriage, managing the breeding rate limitation, advising young people about the effects of too early conception of children and the conceiving of them when too old. All of this is well advised and easily implemented.

As to positive eugenics, I believe Dr. Ramsey has greatly underestimated this. There are too many principles and too many applications under the heading "Positive Eugenics" for us to exclude them in one or several statements.

I don't see solutions forwarded on how to control the mixture between sexual and clonal reproduction—although nothing that Dr. Ramsey said implied that there was. What to do with the mishaps? In normal birth 1 or 2 percent are mishaps. It is certainly easy to suggest as one thing to keep in mind that, if we ever decide on clonal, it must be at least equal to natural production and reproduction in this respect. I don't have any suggestions about how to control it. There is plenty of time to think this through. With respect to the hybrid species that is conscious and walking around, in light of the sanctity of the human individual I don't know how

---

Will the programmed reproduction of man not in fact dehumanize him? Dr. Lederberg responded in his column in the *Washington Post*, 4 November 1967. His reply focused unduly upon the expression "tampering with human genes." He stated that there would be "no greater difficulty about reversing evolutionary mistakes than there were in making them in the first place"—as if that constituted an answer to the serious issues Dr. Kass raised.

Then came a surprising paragraph which, in the light of our foregoing discussion, the reader may not without reason regard as disingenuous and less than forthright. I cite it now because in it Dr. Lederberg repaired to preventive eugenics and to a quite proper practice of genetics in medical service to the lives of people. "In fact, the anxiety about genetic intervention is almost certainly not directed to anything really likely to happen. We probably will welcome any chance to alleviate the impact of mongolism, schizophrenia, diabetes, or dwarfism. Probably what is more alarming is the abstract concept that 'man will control his own destiny.' Man as manipulator is too much of a god; as object, too much of a machine."

This strategic retreat happened again in the testimony of Drs. Kornberg and Lederberg before the Senate Subcommittee on Government Research on the Mondale bill, according to one newspaper account. Senator Ribicoff used scare-language in his question, "Do you see this leading to a master race?" "No, at least probably not," was the answer. Then, instead of a frank discussion of what it is believed will be going on in laboratories at a very early date, both scientists said they saw this as only a remote possibility—unless, said Dr. Kornberg, by "master race, you mean *healthier people*" (italics added). ("Dr. Barnard Rejects Curbs on Doctors," byline Victor Cohn, *Washington Post*, 9 March 1968.) This, not doctoring that nonpatient, the human race, is the object of medical care.

to react to this; it is too difficult to understand the measure against which we judge.

Religion opened with a strong voice in this conference. Yesterday we were told that human life must not be interrupted after fertilization, almost irrespective of the consequences to liberty and the pursuit of happiness. The answer to Dr. Ramsey's challenge of yesterday is obvious: Does not the moral logic contain or imply articles of faith which are necessary assumptions only for those who accept the articles of faith? How can he defend an absolute value for human life in this day and time? What is this reverence for human life that seems to exclude all other life? This would be the argument of modern biology. Actually, in addition to the problem that he devoted his entire paper to, the fundamental criticism that I could propose is that I hardly think that Lederberg's scheme is worthy of a whole manuscript. To me, there have been proposed three different schemes, each by geneticists. Muller was dismissed in one sentence and Bettell was not mentioned. Perhaps I should stop here.

DR. RAMSEY: I thank you for your comments. There are issues here which demand that people from all kinds of professions move toward an understanding, meeting together about these matters. This means that scientists in the field will have to make some of the efforts. There are issues here as to what one is going to say as far as public policy is concerned. These issues are larger than a specific faith stance. One of the criticisms attributed to me involves a claim I would not make: that reverence of life depends on our faith. Certainly more is at stake than trying to persuade one or the other of the faith. The issue here is whether people in chemistry and related fields can begin to propose where ethics should go. We must acknowledge that specialists presently govern the activities and make the determinations within that community. Now, our concern is not just with the connection between ethics and reverence of life, or sanctity of life. What was challenged here is the very notion of reverence of life, the ethics itself.

I am certain that if we are going to be fully rational with respect to the borderline prospects that are ahead, there must be broad consideration of these problems, unless the people who are ethically concerned are to be set down by their fellow scientists as fanatics. We are now fully irrational unless we are willing to bring to light the ethical premise, and examine the problem to see whether or not in the mind of the people it goes against life. The ethics of control is an issue we have to get out into the open and bring under full and open scrutiny.

5. Technological Devices in Medical Care

The subject of spare parts replacement of functions and prosthetic reduplication of human activity was presented in a scintillating way by Dr. Joseph Fletcher. He addressed himself to a question rather similar to that of Ramsey, in effect: "Shall we rebuild a man?"

The whole spare parts program in health care involves a pressing ethical dimension. Prostheses and orthoses of many types are now available. Numerous manual functions are capable of reduplication. Artificial organs, for example, dialysis machines, the iron lung, and the ventricular bypass, add to the measure in which we can supplement or reduplicate human function. The computer is potentially a reduplication of the central nervous system. The ethical question clearly emerges: What are the limits in rebuilding man? Do you automatically reduplicate each function that fails? Problems of a personal nature as well as problems of social-political import in this area were raised and weighed during the session.

Dr. Fletcher is as responsible as any religious thinker today for the lively discussion of ethics that characterizes our time. His writing and speaking in the areas of business ethics and medical ethics have been extensive.[1] *A director of the American Society for Christian Ethics, he is currently Robert Treat Paine Professor of Social Ethics at the Episcopal Theological School in Cambridge, Massachusetts.*

Included here also are excerpts from the responses of Dr. Carlos Vallbona, Professor of Rehabilitation at Baylor College of Medicine, and Dr. Ramsey.

---

[1] Some of his pertinent writings are listed in the Bibliography.

Technological Devices in Medical Care

Joseph Fletcher

A mass circulation magazine recently ran a two-page advertisement by General Electric which showed an eight-year-old boy at play in the fields. The ad explained how an implanted pacemaker maintains a 92 per minute beat in Brian Coe's heart. The caption read, "This boy's heart runs on batteries." Such devices are at work in patients from six-month-old girls to ninety-four-year-old men. "Helping people live longer," said the advertisement, "is progress of the most important kind."

The Terms and Ideas We Use

When we submit technological devices to ethical analysis, we need first to be clear about what we mean by "technological" and what we mean by a "device." Too often, I think, we use the concept of technology in a narrow way, doing less than justice to its practitioners and their triumphs. In the popular image, for example, the term "technology" usually connotes a gadget, a mechanical tool or arrangement of some kind. Indeed, the common error is precisely to conceive of technology as a matter of mechanics. And the same is true of devices—they are thought of as more or less ingeniously "devised" mechanical tools or arrangements. But this mechanical model is far from adequate for the ethical evaluation of technology as it plays its part (an increasingly essential part) in medical care.

Arnold Toynbee has spoken of "technology's relentless progress," and it is my own belief that technology, with its often revolutionary innovations in how we do things, is the source or cause of the most pressing problems of ethics. Either it poses perennial problems of good and evil in significantly new forms, or it confronts us with new problems of conscience, new in the sense that they are unanticipated and often even seemingly bizarre. This happens in medicine fully as much as in industry or war or communications or any other field. In a moment we shall have occasion to look at some typical examples.

But first, there are various ways to think technology. Another word for it could be "techniquery." It is indeed a matter of devices or of "devising" ways and means. It is at bottom a matter of process, innovation, method. Nevertheless, technology is far more than merely ingenious. It is a knowledgeable combination of information and skill, of know-what (science) and know-how (technology). In its bluntest definition, it is applied science. It is the scientifically disciplined and sophisticated invention of devices to serve the ends or goals or "goods" we cherish. In medicine these ends are health and life and psychophysical well-being. As a matter of means and ends, therefore, technology is of the greatest direct ethical concern. Perhaps the best definition is Webster's: "the totality of the means employed to provide objects necessary for human sustenance and comfort."[2]

But let me repeat: technology—perhaps especially in medicine—is far from being a matter of mechanics only. The "hardware" is less important than the "software." In medicine, the systems engineering of technology is not only mechanical but also chemical, biological, physical, psychological, and surgical. Hyperbaric chambers put chemistry and physics to use in crisis surgery. The use of hormones to regulate both primary and secondary sexual conditions is an example of how almost all of these disciplines may be harnessed together by medicine. Even surgery is involved in some cases, for example, in transexual alterations. A cardiology device such as a blood-pressure sensor or tiny electronic monitoring device, so small (five one-hundredths of an inch) that it can be injected into an artery with a hypodermic needle and then maneuvered into a ventricle to send signals to a recording machine in an intensive care unit, is obviously a union of physics, biology, and surgery. And a left-ventricle assist-device, especially if it is of synthetic or plastic material (such as DuPont's Lycra) adds chemistry to the team. Artificial insemination, "one of the best kept

[2] *Webster's Seventh New Collegiate Dictionary* (Springfield, Mass.: G. & C. Merriam Company, 1967).

secrets in American medicine," is another example of how technology in medicine entails psychology, physiology, biology, and often also physics and mechanics, as in the centrifugal collection of sperm for homologous inseminations to overcome a husband's low sperm count. Or a battery and tiny transmitter may be mounted on a pessary to signal temperature changes following ovulation in order to assist in overcoming sterility, or to make the rhythm "method" more accurate, or even to give some control over the sex of offspring. All resuscitation techniques for the drowned or frozen, for cardiac arrest, cardio-vascular lesions, spontaneous hypoglycemia, and the like, involve technologies of a multidisciplinary kind.

In this context it is worth remembering that cybernetics itself is a conflation of biology (especially brain physiology) and communications theory, automatic control mechanics (especially feedback), mathematics, and logic. Strange as it may seem, physicians in this era need to be good engineers as well. Much of the work on medical-surgical technology—for example, in heart, lung, and limb renewals, replacements, and supportive prosthetics (so-called cyborg medicine)—has come from people who are both. I think in this connection of Nikolai Amasov of the Kiev Institute of Thoracic Surgery, and Mikhail Bykhovsky of the cybernetics laboratory in the Vishnesky Institute of Surgery in the Soviet Union.[3] They have their counterparts in America, Europe, and around the world.

The Influence of Technology

Technology by this date is fully in service to medicine. As a matter of fact, it is changing more than just man's environment and his tools: it is changing man himself. Hence our recent more mature and scientific interest in ecology. "Once men start down the technological road," says Roger Revelle, "they cannot turn back. Once they have bitten into the fruit of the tree of knowledge, there can be no return to Eden."[4] As I put it sometime ago at the Mayo medical center, we have reached the end of the age of in-

[3] See Y. Saparina, *Cybernetics Within Us,* trans. V. Talmy (Moscow: Peace Publishers, 1966).

[4] *Boston Globe,* 1 January 1967.

nocence, that is, of ignorance, and the end of ignorance means the end of alibis and excuses.[5]

Every widening or deepening of our knowledge of reality and our control of its forces adds to our ethical problems; knowledge and control are the ingredients of both freedom and responsibility. Less and less are we the helpless and therefore nonmoral victims of whatever life happens to bring to us—and by "life" here I mean not only circumstances but the vital principle of biological life itself. Knowledge and virtue have always been coupled, as by Confucius and Socrates—an association recently reexamined by the English biologist C. H. Waddington in his essay *The Ethical Animal,* [6] and by Rene Dubos in *Adapting Man.*[7]

As Pascal thought, the problem of ethics is *"travailler à bien penser,"* "to work hard at good thinking." Not feeling or guessing, but thinking and knowing. "Let us," he said, "strive to think well—therein is the principle of morality."[8] And Kant called ethics "practical reason." In this spirit we can say that the heart of the problems of medical ethics is the science and technology at stake in them, along with a willingness to see our values and goals in the fresh light of fresh developments, and even to add to or abstract from them as the data suggests. I would be the first to echo the opinion of J. Robert Oppenheimer, who said, "I believe the strength and soundness of Christian sensibility, the meaning of love and charity, have changed the world at least as much as technological developments." But, as Oppenheimer suggests, I want to insist that it is in love working with technology, not in love alone, that we find the key to human hopes.

Biology is the great new realm of technological change, and medicine is its chief beneficiary. After the First World War our cultural emphasis lay on the social and behavioral sciences. Then it shifted at the time of the Second World War to the physical sciences, due in the main to new frontiers in nuclear research. But by the sixties the greatest excitement was being found in the

---

[5] See Joseph Fletcher, "Medicine's Scientific Developments and Ethical Problems," in *Dialogue in Medicine and Theology,* ed. Dale White (Nashville: Abingdon Press, 1968), pp. 103-33.

[6] C. H. Waddington, *The Ethical Animal* (Chicago: University of Chicago Press, 1960).

[7] Rene Dubos, *Adapting Man* (New Haven: Yale University Press, 1965).

[8] H. F. Stewart, ed., Blaise *Pascal's Pensées* (New York: Pantheon, 1950), p. 83.

biological sciences. Of what was once called "pure biology" there is little left in these days of biochemistry, psychobiology, biophysics, microbiology, bionautics, and the like.

It was "only yesterday" that so much started to happen in biology. Jean Rostand tells us how Viguier only a few decades ago made fun of what he called the "chemical citizens, the sons of Madame Sea-Urchin and Monsieur Chloride of Magnesium," but now we speak calmly of the solitary generation of creatures by artificial parthenogenesis, and of diploid rather than sexual reproduction.[9] Ancient alchemy dreamed of the "creation" of life, and now—at least theoretically in a scientific sense—it is possible, given Kornberg's partial success in first producing a synthetic virus containing DNA, the basic substance of all life, and then in getting it to reproduce itself in a living cell.

The momentum of our scientific-technical development is hard to grasp—and nowhere more so than in medicine. By leaps and bounds it proceeds, in invention (finding new methods), in innovation (introducing new methods into use), and in diffusion (spreading their use). Lots of it comes like serendipity, unexpected profit in side effects. After all, we need to remember, Roentgen had no real idea what he was doing when all of a sudden he saw the skeleton of his own hand. And it has been said that if all the wisest medical people in 1890 had been asked to suggest the next important invention, none would have mentioned the X ray.

I have two dictionaries in my study, and while I still prefer the 1913 Webster for literary purposes, I have to rely upon a 1967 edition because the old one of half a century ago has almost none of the language of present-day technological discourse. This is a hundredfold truer of medical dictionaries. For example, the intrauterine devices have reopened the question whether conception is accomplished at fertilization or at nidation. They have also reopened the definition of abortion: Does it cover direct interference with the development of a preuterine or unimplanted zygote? Or only of uterine material?

More substantially than the words we use, our knowledge and data are mounting so fast that although we have a hundred times as much to know as in 1900, by A.D. 2000 there will be a thousand

[9] Jean Rostand, *Can Man Be Modified?* trans. Jonathan Griffin (New York: Basic Books, 1959), p. 11.

times as much. There is a tremendous explosion of information, investigation, and publication, and our archival and bibliographic methods are already antiquated in spite of computerized retrieval. In fact, specialties are so fractured by the knowledge expansion that a "generalist" nowadays is just what a specialist was only a couple of decades ago.

As a consequence of this complexity, medicine turns more and more to computerized diagnosis. A LINC (Laboratory Instrument Computer) quickly does what a clinical interview takes hours to do. For example, the answer to such a question as "Have you ever had hives?" triggers the LINC to go on to maybe four hundred queries about related allergies, whereas doctors would never think of them all. This multiphasic screening will mean the revelation of hidden diseases cybernetically. As things stand now, for every cervical cancer diagnosed, dozens go undetected, and so with diabetes, and so on. And as computers (especially analog) get more complicated they will probably find heretofore unsuspected and undescribed diseases and maladies. Even in isolated communities physicians could connect by telephone landlines to central computers—like a central catalogue for bibliographic inquiries from libraries—and get diagnoses in fifteen seconds over teletype. This is what the combination of "hardware" and "software" in technology can do. Names like Pasteur, Lister, Roentgen, and the Curies will, of course, have their successors in the technological age, but far more will be achieved corporately and by team work without any hero mystique, because of technology's built-in process of interdependence or collective achievement.

The Ethical Problems Posed

The picture of what has happened in the technology of medicine and paramedical care fills us, ambivalently, with fear and confidence, assurance and doubt—both as to the facts themselves and as to the value-meaning of the facts, their ethical significances. For example, how are we to regard the prospect of human hibernation for short periods (hours or days) and later for longer periods (months or years), as cryonics develops from its present uses as "deep freeze" for surgical purposes? What will the surgical use of laser beams ultimately entail (besides the dangers of the so-called death ray)? Genetic control of the basic human constitution by microbiological manipulation of "code" material, DNA and RNA, is at hand. Is there any cause to be squeamish or chary about using techniques for cosmetic changes of human features, figure, complexion, skin color, and even physique? Or the more radical technology of chemotherapy in controlling fatigue, relaxation, alertness, mood, sleep, personality, perception, and fantasies? Lurking behind all such questioning is the factor of control: We wonder whether we may establish and exercise management of the very essentials of personal identity and existence. The question really is not whether we can but whether we should. We can do it, but the ethical question is: Ought we to?

Chemotherapy is far less challenging morally than the immediate or prospective manipulations of psychopharmacology, for example, in changing the chemical composition of the nervous system, its neurons and chemical transmitters of impulses, or than the chemical control and improvement of memory and learning (even, theoretically, programmed dreams). The very concepts of choice, chance, self, and rationality, so central to classical or traditional reasoning, may have to be altered or even "reconceptualized."

Take the notion of "identity," a notion so prominent in the current rhetoric of psychology, especially under the influence of Erikson's thesis about the identity crisis. Given the present and future trends in cyborg medicine, one may well ask: Who is it that functions physiologically with borrowed or artificial veins and arteries (whether synthetic or plastic), bone structures, prosthetic devices, cardiac implants—including even donated aortas or whole hearts—audio and visual aids, manipulators and pedipulators, donated kidneys, or artificial dialysis for kidney function, artificial kidneys and hearts powered by isotopic energy, and many other technological devices, logically ending in a sort of *ultima ratio* with transplanted brains?

Who is the child born as a result of predetermined sex, germinal selection, genetic control, and artificial mutations—and after birth modified not only by cyborg technology but by chemical and electronic means, for example, by effective appetite controls and weight controls, electric brain stimulation by electrodes and surgical subcuts, endocrine alterations, and the like?

For just as we once reached the point at which diabetics could regulate the sugar in their blood systems, so we will have autocontrol of mood and intelligence. Who, then, is who? How will we think of it when theoretical brain transplants become operational? As they say, today's "science fiction" is tomorrow's science.

Who *is* the recipient patient—is he the preoperative person or the donor? This kind of basic conceptual question, like the one about when and what is death, will inevitably change not only the language but also the mental constructs with which we think about moral values, ethical responsibility, and even the very notion of the moral agent himself.

What are our licit or morally justifiable choices, initiatives, and purposes as we employ the technology of medicine? What are the values we should seek or preserve—such as freedom from pain, health, euphoria, even life itself—and in what order of relative desirability are we to rank them? What comes first as the *summum bonum,* in the sense that, if necessary, all else is to be subordinated or sacrificed? Life? Self-image? Personal survival? Social welfare? In the conventional wisdom nearly all such questions have been almost ignored, or their answers complacently assumed. But technology has a way of undermining conventions, of changing the world, and with it our values and priorities.

The Problem of Control

As I remarked earlier, my own opinion is that, morally, the heart of the matter is control. The question is whether human beings may choose or make the conditions of life, health, and death. (I am sure that death control, as in direct or indirect euthanasia, is as much a part of modern medicine as birth control and health control are.) The key to control, however, is initiative. True control of life puts the initiative in man's hands; that is, it is a matter of choice. Nothing not chosen has ethical importance. Babies born by chance rather than choice may be precious, but their birth is amoral if not actually immoral. A patient who dies in personality-blotting suffering, or after personality is gone and irretrievable, may be an object of compassion, but his actual dying is nonmoral and his own relationship to it is either amoral or immoral, as is that of his medical servants as well.

What we do when we can do it, by our own choice, initiative, and purposiveness, is moral action—either right or wrong, as the case may be. If we refuse to do what we can when we can, on the ground that we may not or ought not to take the initiative, this is nonmoral and antiethical—I would even add "subhuman," because truly human acts are moral, that is, free and responsible. For example, not to take the initiative by using a Bennett valve and mask in a case of respiratory failure on the operating table might in a concrete situation be a responsible decision to let the patient go. Such a decision might, for example, be made for a nonegenarian patient with grievously metastasized cancer. But *never* to revive artificially a patient whose respiration fails would be immoral, that is, it would be a refusal to exercise initiative and choice. It would be irresponsible and therefore immoral.

A great deal of ethical reasoning in the past has been of this immoral kind—arguing against initiative and human control on grounds that it is allegedly "unnatural" or "against nature." That kind of ethics simply cannot survive in a technological civilization. "Nature" and "human nature" are no more fixed and finished than any of the other concepts moralists like to posit. In Catholic moral theology it used to be held that we are only tenants of our bodies, that we may not alter them because we have only their usufruct, not their dominion. As stewards, not proprietors, of our bodies we have charge only of the *bene esse*, not of the *esse*. Hence, no mutilation was morally justified, except to preserve life. This ruled out donations of organs such as kidneys and ovaries, as well as free decision for or against the new transformations possible as a result of scientific and technical development. But that old morality of nature is being superceded, happily, by a new morality of love. What this means, for example, is that those who have courage will gladly risk the sacrifice of one of their kidneys for a friend, thus deliberately reducing their own survival quotient by half; or that a nun who has embraced the vocation of childlessness will eagerly donate an ovary to a sterile patient.

The new morality of situation ethics has little patience with those who object in principle to heart transplants from cadaveric donors. Such a position has been taken by Dr. Werner Forssmann, chief surgeon at the Düsseldorf Evangelical Hospital and Nobel prize winner in medicine for 1956. In commenting on Christian Barnard's successful transplants in South Africa, he said such transplants are morally dangerous because they involve a third person, the donor, as well as the doctor and the recipient patient, and because they offend against the medical rule *nil nacere,* "hurt nothing." There is a danger, of course, that surgeons will sacrifice the chances of one patient for the sake of the other, that this will lead, for example, to executing criminals in order to get vital organs, and to an inequitable tendency to select recipients on the basis of wealth, personal friendship, or politics. On the other hand, most Catholic moralists already say that "it is morally permissible to transfer parts from a corpse to a living person,"[10] and in Dr. Barnard's interview with the pope no objections were voiced. I am myself convinced that we must stick to the maxim of most moralists, *abusus non tollit usum,* "the abuse of the thing does not bar its use." As Raymond Queneau once said, "The people who whine about naughty robots and inhuman machinery have never proved anything except their own lack of imagination and fear of liberty."[11] As the old saw put it, "conscience" gets a lot of credit that belongs to cold feet.

Dr. Forssmann also believes that it was wrong to put a pig's liver in a dying woman in Buenos Aires—presumably on the ground that heterografts or xenogenic (i.e., interspecific) transplants are "unnatural." By this logic we would, for example, have to give up the transplantation of monkeys' thymus glands into cancerous patients' thighs in an effort to let the antibodies help in the struggle against the neoplasm. This will be a hard kind of classicism to maintain as immunosuppressive techniques overcome the rejection reaction, and as better antigen typing and tissue preservation are developed.[12] It is a matter of time, that is all, until herds of animals are raised directly for human spare parts—cows, swine, chimpanzees, and the like. Already, barely on the threshold of transplant technique, we have only a sad short-supply of paired organs (livers, lungs, hearts) for postmortem donation, and of nonpaired organs (kidneys, ovaries, testes) for pre- or postmortem donation. Even if we could discourage the present subethical practice of burying or burning (cremating) precious vital organs—here is immorality ritualized—there still would be a need for interspecific supplies.

[10] See, e.g., Robert White, M.D., and Charles Curran, Th.D., "The Morality of Human Transplants," *The Sign* (March 1968), pp. 19-30.

[11] Rostand, *op. cit.*, p. 62.

[12] Rejection may be solved by studying how mothers for nine months avoid rejecting the fetus which consists of foreign or alien tissue! The secret might well be in the placenta. (In all animal life, even the lowly earthworm, the rejection mechanism occurs.)

One of the ethical issues at stake, then, is whether any procedure or process is, as such, to be proscribed as always wrong for some intrinsic reason. A hundred years ago dissection of human bodies was forbidden, so that grave robber and medical student meant the same thing; yet all that is gone by now—a mythology demythologized. For some people abortion is still held to be immoral in all cases except when necessary to preserve the life and/or health of a patient. But unlike this absolutism (really a mystique) of the old morality, the new morality decides the right or the wrong of medical treatments relatively, according to the factors in each situation. If, for example, there is at least a 25 percent chance that a PKU child (phenylketonuric) will be born of a union of PKU heterozygotes, producing a retarded child, why not abort? Especially if normal children can be adopted or conceived by artificial insemination from a donor? Why submit to the cruel workings of subhuman, physical nature? Technology by its very principle and method substitutes human control for nature's control—and holds, indeed, that control is a word appropriate only to the moral decisions of people and inappropriate to the determinism of mindless processes. As a writer in the *British Medical Journal* once put it very simply, "Each case must be judged on its merits."

Two Key Questions

Among the ethical problems posed by modern technological medicine and calling for fresh and honest ethical analysis, some arise around the initiative which physicians and surgeons must exercise on behalf of their patients. Let me mention just two of them: (1) deciding when a patient is dead, and (2) deciding whether to include a clinical experiment in the treatment plan for a patient.

1) After the Washkansky and Blaiberg heart transplants in late 1967 and early 1968, Dr. Christian Barnard said that "certain death" is shown by total lack of nerve reflexes, respiration, and heart activity.[13] Personally, I doubt if that is a realistic definition of death; almost certainly it will have to be replaced by a cerebral definition, which says that death has occurred when there is a flat EEG reading for something like twenty-four hours, more or less. The issue is: Does human life exist apart from mentation? But even accepting Barnard's definition, what is the morally requisite *cause* of the

[13] *Time,* 15 December 1967, p. 64.

absence of reflexes, and so on? Was it murder or death which made the donor's heart available in the Washkansky transplant? The donor, Denise Darvall, was being kept alive by respirator, and then her neurosurgeon, deciding that she could not survive more than a few days, and with the permission of the patient's father, stopped the respirator. Her heart went to Washkansky, and one of her kidneys to a ten-year-old boy, Jonathan Van Wyk. Dr. William Sweet and other neurosurgeons at Massachusetts General Hospital are now canvassing research and clinical physicians throughout the world, to see if empirical experience indicates when we can give up hope of a "useful recovery" from coma.

Rabbi Immanuel Jakobovits, chief rabbi in Britain and a leading authority on Orthodox Jewish medical ethics, says, "Even a fraction of life is precious. Therefore, no one must hasten the death of a donor."[14] For my part, I hold to my view, as reported in *Newsweek* apropos the Barnard and Kantrowitz heart transplants, that "speeding up a donor's death, when death is 'positively' inevitable, may be justified if the transplant provides another human with valuable life."[15] It is to be noted, by the way, that I say "may"—if, for example, the donor is brain-damaged irreversibly, or is going to die in a matter of hours or days, or will be executed for a capital crime if he recovers, and so on. The same problem has arisen with respect to kidney transplants in various parts of the world.

Who is right: I and Barnard or Rabbi Jakobovits? And why so? What justice is there in the saying that in cases like those in Capetown the surgeon "kills" his patient (I mean the recipient this time), then rescues him by artificial means, then "kills" the donor patient, and then transplants?[16] Will the need of vital organs cause doctors to do less than all they can to keep donors alive? Does it make any difference if the donor's situation is benign or malign—that is, can we be situational about it, or must there be a universal principle by which to make moral judgments? When is a human life no longer worth saving? These ethical problems posed by technology in medi-

[14] *Newsweek*, 18 December 1967, p. 87. Rabbi Jakobovits is the author of *Jewish Medical Ethics* (New York: Bloch, 1959).

[15] *Newsweek*, 18 December 1967, p. 87.

[16] The problem already exists in thoracic surgery, in open-heart procedures. The patient's temperature is lowered, suspending circulation, and then he is ex-sanguinated, running his blood into a mechanical system. Brain waves go flat. This is physiological and cerebral death—temporarily.

cine are profound in their significance. Two five-year-old girls, for example, are dying of renal failure; a third child is killed in an auto accident, but only one of her kidneys survives intact; and tissues and blood typing show that both patients are good recipients. Which one gets the available kidney? Sometimes we can only flip a coin.

2) Is it not true that good medicine has to combine the therapeutic and the experimental? Can we really make a nice distinction between them? At a meeting of the American Cancer Society I overheard remarks like these:

– The concept of absolute safety for a drug is a myth.
– It's difficult to find anything that is not toxic if given in the right dose.
– So far as we know, the silicones can be implanted in humans for various purposes and cause no toxic reaction. But we know of other things which later turned out to be cancer-causing. Not enough time has elapsed for a final answer.
– It is possible that any substance can cause birth defects if given to a pregnant woman at the right time.
– We would have no drugs left if all the drugs that caused birth defects in rats and rabbits were banned.
– We really are abysmally ignorant about how to treat many diseases. It's conceivable that a new treatment may be better than the present one, and that the ethical thing to do is to test the new treatment on half the patients.
– Many serious drug reactions can't be anticipated by tests on animals. Actual testing on humans is the only way.

Just because it was a "first" of its kind, though hardly new in the sense of plunging into the unknown, some people called the Washkansky transplant an "experiment." But Dr. Barnard retorted, "I wouldn't like to call this operation an experiment–it was treatment of a sick patient."[17] It was that, but it was also experimental, inevitably, and rightly so. When did cardiac catheters cease to be experimental and become an accepted diagnostic procedure? Let's not forget that the first lumbar puncture in a Boston hospital resulted in the doctor's being fired for it.

Imagine this scene, in a great and justly famous hospital: The house officer has given a cancer patient a dose of Cytoxan to break

[17] *Time,* 29 December 1967, p. 32.

down the cancer cells, retard the metastasis, and see how long it will hold death off. Then a nurse comes in, calling out, "The patient is dying." The doctor says, "Yes, but give him Eramine" (a drug which is an artificial respiration elevator, lifting the breathing threshold). He wants, of course, to keep the patient alive for a little longer in order to see how much effect the Cytoxan can have. Now was this research or treatment? Was the patient alive? If it was research rather than treatment, when was the point of difference reached? Was it ethical? How well equipped are we to deal with such clinically persistent questions?

The Nuremberg Code (1947), the Declaration of Geneva (at the 1948 General Assembly of the World Medical Association), the 1964 Declaration of Helsinki, the American Medical Association's ethical code and guidelines—constantly revised by its House of Delegates—all of these insist (among other things) that ethical experimentation, especially when it is clinical, shall be by the patient's voluntary consent, that it shall be based on prior animal tests, and that it shall be safe. I challenge these pretentious moralizings, just as actual experience in clinical experimentation challenges them. There are a hundred and one tests of new drugs and new procedures and devices which cannot be tested on animals; they have to be tried on human beings. And they cannot be adequately explained to the layman lying in the bed, so that "competent consent" is impossible. Isoniazide for tuberculosis, for example, will cause lung cancer in mice if given in the same dose indicated for humans. It is difficult to find a beneficial substance that is not toxic when given in the right dose. All experienced research and clinical physicians will testify that the concept of absolute safety for a drug or procedure is a myth. There just is no escape from finite, and more than finite, probability.

The Social Dimension

When Senator Seymour Thaler of the New York State Assembly introduced a bill restricting research initiative in the medical care of children, university and secular physicians in pediatrics and other branches of medicine promptly testified that if such a law had existed in the early 1950's polio would still be running rampant, measles would be rife, and rubella would still be the widespread hazard it used to be. Ethical issues of this kind raise the whole complicated problem of the social interest as distinguished from individual interests and from interpersonal and professional ethics. We cannot help being troubled by such over-simple ethics as the rule of the Federal Drug Administration and the National Institutes of Health that the patient comes first, in his individual capacity. Frontier medicine and research are ethically involved with far more than the individual patient, and the traditional professional principle of always putting the patient's welfare first is logically inconsistent with the social and undiscriminating purposes of medical investigation.

For example, the common practice of double-blind test runs (perhaps on a new antibiotic) shows this sidetracking of individual welfare. By giving some patients the new treatment, some the old, and some only a placebo—no patient or subject knowing which is which—there is obviously a discrimination in their risks and potential benefit. The fact that their roles are determined impersonally by a chance-distribution does not change the fact.[18]

Ethical plain speaking calls for a hardnosed formula: the welfare of the many comes before the welfare of the few, or, if you prefer, the individual may rightly be sacrificed to the social good. It is ethical infantilism to suppose that there is a comfortable harmony between the private and the social interest. It was never shown to be so by the laissez faire theory of Manchester economics, and it cannot be shown in the realms of medicine and sanitation. Technology is thus in one sense impersonal, even though its ultimate aim is the benefit of as many persons as possible. We have to "mathematicate" our moral decisions, our choices between value-alternatives. This is properly enough called "statistical morality."[19] Ethics cannot escape calculative interests, playing the numbers game, nose or head counting. We have to make responsible choices in medicine, all the way from an almost one-to-one choice by selection committees trying to decide who shall live and who shall die when there is only a limited supply of kidney machines available for dialysis, up to such massive enterprises as the historic yellow

[18] This is a much discussed question, but see "The Changing Mores of Biomedical Research," *Annals of Internal Medicine* 67, supp. 7, no. 3, pt. 2 (September 1967): 47 ff.

[19] There is some chance in everything. Four ladies playing bridge in Indiana in 1967 were dealt perfect hands—all spades, hearts, diamonds, or clubs. The odds on the deal are 53,644,737,767,488,792,839,237,439,999 to 1.

fever studies in which thousands of ignorant people were inoculated with no hope of personally benefiting. (After all, juries and draft boards also decide who shall die and who shall live.)

The U.S. Public Health Service in 1951-54 tried to destroy the virus of hepatitus. Tests were run on 533 prisoners in three federal penitentiaries. Of these, 130 got the disease, 3 developed hepatic coma, and 2 died. The end result was enormous, immeasurable benefit to mankind. The medical people at the University of Colorado[20] will tell us that we cannot get a "true" consent from prisoners and that they should not be accepted for experiment when they volunteer; surely that is only obstructive moralism.

There are, of course, some problems of statistical morality which are almost too problematic to yield a calculated choice. For example, in Massachusetts it was found that only forty-five out of a half-million babies are born with PKU, but a blood specimen from the neonatal's heel will indicate whether that particular metabolic disorder is present, and this knowledge can help prevent retardates. Its occurrence is only one in thirteen thousand. Is it worth the trouble? Why? Under what circumstances should it cease to be a routine practice? (Incidentally, why should we not "use" retarded babies for experiments we would not impose on other children?)

In an undeveloped country do you direct your attention medically to the young or the old—to the future, or to present need? Why? Why do you take medical aid there in the first place, knowing that although it lowers the death rate it also raises the birth rate, thus lifting the population further and further beyond the supply of food, shelter, and clothing—the present discrepancy already being the source of much starvation, misery, disease and malnutrition, premature aging and mortality. In either case, why do you do this?

"Playing God"

At this point somebody always cries, "You are playing God!" I think the only honest and constructive reply is, "Yes, we are." This is part of the meaning of the Bible's creation and "fall" myths. By gaining know-what and know-how we become responsible, by eating the fruit of the tree of knowledge we make ourselves "like God" —whose superiority is threatened by man's inquiry and invention.

---

[20] See, e.g., Thomas E. Starzl, M.D., "Ethical Problems in Organ Transplantation," *Annals of Internal Medicine* 67, no. 3 (September 1967): 35.

But that old, primitive God is dead, that God of the gaps, the God whose majesty and power derived from man's ignorance. That God was God because of human ignorance and fear, and he has been dying by inches with the advance of human knowledge and the control over life and death which knowledge brings to man. In the matter of human knowledge we are indeed "playing the God of the gaps." If such achievements as extogenetic reproduction, genetic control, and the production (not creation) of life in a test tube shakes anybody's faith, then his God is only one that plugs up the gaps in his knowledge, a hypothesis of ignorance. If we have to say goodbye to God because science solves the mysteries of life and technology gives us control of life, then our God is only a doomed idol.

What we need then is a new God. It is better to believe in God as creator, the creative principle behind all the workings of nature and of human achievement. He is as much the will and the love behind a test tube as behind "natural phenomena." This God can be worshiped as the other no longer can. After all, as Eric Ambler once said, "If there is such a thing as a super-human law, it is administered with subhuman inefficiency."[21]

We must get rid of that obsolete theodicy which imagines that God is not only the cause but the builder of nature and its works, and not only the builder but the manager—so that it is God himself who is the efficient as well as the final cause of earthquake and fire, of life and death, with the logical inference that "interference with nature" (which is precisely what medicine and technology are) is "playing God." That God is dead.

As I have expressed it in the *Atlantic Monthly,* in an article about neonatal defects such as the Down's syndrome, "The belief that God is at work directly or indirectly in all natural phenomena is a form of animism or simple pantheism. If we took it really seriously, all science, including medicine, would die away because we would be afraid to 'dissect God' or tamper with His activity. Such beliefs are a hopelessly primitive kind of God-thought and God-talk, but they hang on long after theologians generally have bid them good-bye."[22]

[21] Eric Ambler, *A Coffin for Dimitrios* (New York: Dell, 1939), p. 9.

[22] Bernard Bard and Joseph Fletcher, "The Right to Die," *Atlantic Monthly* 221, no. 4 (April 1968): 64.

Some decisions are less radically problematic, although equally statistical. For example, we debate whether it is wise to give mass smallpox vaccinations, since postvaccinal encephalitis is fairly common whereas the risk of getting smallpox, at least in industrially mature societies, is not great. How shall we figure the probabilities? Here, it seems to me, the differential consideration is that the risk of getting smallpox is low precisely because of the preventive practice of mass vaccination. But it is not a simple moral question, comparable to "doing all we can for the patient" in clinical medicine.

We are pursued by ambivalences as much as by ambiguities. For example, diabetics were in mortal danger until we found the insulin treatment, yet they still could not risk pregnancy and childbirth. Now we can deliver them safely, but with what result? The result is an increase in diabetes, the spread of a genetic defect. There is always a risk of cancer to kidney recipients from cancerous donors. Synthetics have unexpected side effects, as was found with Chloromycetin (chlorophenicol) which has been connected with leukemia and aplastic anemia. Artificial hearts fueled with isotopic energy may spread radiation. But will that be any worse, or more lethal, than smog, water pollution, air pollution, and highway traffic? After a few years the danger to the cyborg himself can be serious; for example, leukemia may result. If only two or three more years of life are possible, is it worth the trouble and expense of a cardiac substitute? If a patient says, "No, I don't want it," is that suicide? As hemodialysis improves it will foreseeably increase the incidence of suicide, because patients will weary of it all. If a man has been deterioratively paralyzed by a massive stroke and wants to give his heart to a much younger wife because hers is failing, is that suicide? Or is it an act of sacrificial love, realized by technology?

A Serious Conclusion

The Faustian question plagues some people when they discuss technology and morality; it takes possession of them and inhibits them—for example, Jacques Ellul.[23] Will man's growing power over his life and world be his undoing? Like Faust, is he selling his soul for knowledge, power, and riches; and are these things nothing more

[23] See Jacques Ellul, *The Technological Society* (New York: Knopf, 1967), esp. pp. 428-36.

than what Sorokin called "sensate" values?[24] Or, to vary the figure, are we too Promethean, stealing the fire from heaven and the gods —to our own mortal danger?

Jean Rostand is right to warn us, "Let us not give ourselves the airs of demigods, or even of demiurges, when we have only been petty magicians."[25] We do not want to be trapped by a Promethean intoxication, or in a bad bargain of Faustian proportions. And we must not suppose that know-how, as in technology, is of itself enough to show us what is good or worth seeking. On the contrary, we must guard against what Veblen called "the trained incapacity of the specialist," his inability to consider what lies outside his expertise. Perhaps the correct model for modern medicine, in its partnership with the engineers and biologists, is the space probe program of the National Aeronautics and Space Administration in which the design and fabrication of hardware and the operations system are all subjected to a careful testing of their impact on the astronauts themselves, the human needs at stake. Good science (which is itself an ethical phrase) unites facts and values. As Lawrence Granberg has put it, "The very language of our most basic science, quantum mechanics, is the language of expectation and of probability amplitudes."[26]

Kant said two things filled him with awe: the starry heavens above and the moral law within.[27] If, by the first, he meant a sincere humility before the order and power of nature, we can agree; but not if he meant simply acceptance of nature without human interference or manipulation. As to the moral imperative, the "oughtness" of human beings, if he meant the sense of obligation and aspiration, especially to and for human welfare, we can go along with Kant, but not if by "law" he meant ethical rules, or final or universal or "natural" prescriptions of right and wrong regardless of changing needs and situations. There are no hard and fast rules, no fixed norms, no moral recipes.

[24] See Pitirim A. Sorokin, *Social and Cultural Dynamics* (New York: American Book Co., 1937).

[25] Rostand, *op. cit.*, p. 25.

[26] Lawrence Granberg, unpublished paper in the physics department at the University of Virginia, Charlottesville, Virginia.

[27] Emmanuel Kant, *Critique of Practical Reason*, trans. T. K. Abbott (London: Longmans Green & Co., 1923), p. 260.

Dr. Delford Stickel at Duke's medical center has declared that situation ethics, as I have formulated it, "provides a useful and helpful frame of reference within which to deal with the moral aspects" of medical problems, and that it "can foster a quality of responsibility which is in keeping with the best traditions of Western medicine."[28] Let me add, then, that we can only have a choice between three methods of moral decision-making: (1) moral absolutism, (2) anomic indifference, and (3) pragmatic situation ethics.

The first, absolutist ethics, has been the traditional method. Life and death are regarded as a divine monopoly, dependent on the will of God—either directly by special providence or indirectly through delegated processes of nature, presumably including such devices as sexual passion, menstrual cycles, senescence, gangrene, melanoma, and heart failure. On this view it has been wrong to try to be "equal with God" by exerting birth and death control, to say nothing of our many forms of health control.

The second method, the anomic and indifferent (acedic) one, is unconcerned about whether medical control is good or evil. It looks upon such questions as "adiaphora," morally neutral. On this basis we could be eager either to push technology or to restrain it without regard to right-wrong questions, merely accepting human controls as self-validating and *sui justificatis*.

The third alternative, situation ethics, finds technology neither good nor evil in and of itself. Its standard of the good is human well-being; and technology at any place, in any time, of any form, is therefore right or wrong according to whether it detracts or contributes to the good, that is, human need.

This morality finds life good sometimes, and death good sometimes—depending on the situation, on the case or the context. Life is not good in itself, nor is death evil as such. Drugs and prosthetics and transplants, all forms of medical techniquery, are subject to the same ethical contingency. The question to ask about any technological device is not what is right or which one is good, but *when* are they right and *when* are they good. The answer is never prefabricated, in heaven or on earth. The decision lies with us. The age of innocence is gone. We have eaten the apple, the fruit of the tree of knowledge.

[28] Delford L. Stickel, M.D., "Ethical and Moral Aspects of Transplantation," *Monographs in the Surgical Sciences* (Baltimore: Williams and Wilkins, 1966), 3, no. 4: 292.

Katherine Mansfield once said, "At the end, truth is the only thing worth having; it's more thrilling than love, more joyful and more passionate." She was mistaken. Truth is sought for love's sake, not for its own sake. And love is for people—patients, neighbors, family and friends, fellow human beings.

* * *

DR. VALLBONA: To present to you the view of the practicing physician is indeed a difficult task. It is difficult because certainly we are beset with problems. Technological advancements in the care of our patients also bring forth new problems, and we recognize them.

There's a Spanish saying that when an ailment is shared by many it provides comfort to the idiot. At the risk of being considered an idiot, I cannot help but feel comfort by the fact that our problems are shared by many, and that as long as we have people like Dr. Fletcher who are giving us some solutions or some alternatives for these problems, or at least providing for us a path to follow when we are confronted by these problems, I think we can proceed with our medical mission with greater certainty.

I would like to suggest a few things now. In the practice of medicine in our nation I think we are confronted with three major objectives. One is to provide cure to the patient, and another is to provide respite from suffering. But now we are recognizing a third objective—to provide for our patients a better life. I think technological developments have put in our hands some instruments that may help us in providing a better quality of life. However, I think we have to recognize—and Dr. Fletcher has done this marvelously for us—that dangers are ahead with technological advancements. It is possible that we may have capabilities that transcend some of the limitations of the designer. And this was quite well put by Norbert Weiner when he said, "Machines can and do transcend some of the limitations of their designers, and in doing so they may be both effective and dangerous."[29] Dr. Fletcher has clearly stated for us

[29] Norbert Weiner, "Some Moral and Technical Consequences of Automation," *Science* 131, no. 3410 (6 May 1960): 1355.

that we have to weigh indeed the potential effectiveness and the potential danger of technology.

How do we look at this from the physician's standpoint? As I see it, we are in the center of big issues and dilemmas. I'd like to mention a few in the area of the computer in medicine.

There is the dilemma of putting privileged information into computer files, knowing that whatever is in the computer is easily accessible to people. If we continue, it may come to pass that the choice of life and death will be made not by a human being, but by a computer.

There is the possible dilemma that lies in the overruling of the computer's decision by the physician's choice. The physician may feel that the computer has made the wrong choice and he may overrule its decision. But will society accept the time-tested conscientious judgment and decision of the physician over that of the computer? This is indeed a dilemma. In a mature society I think we can follow the path of choice without any difficulties; but what if we were to do this in a vicious society? The possibilities are endlessly unpleasant—and you know in the practice of medicine we are confronted with this many times in legal litigation. This is certainly one of the problems we are facing.

Another problem involves the supplying or delivering of technological advances to the people that need them. It's fine and dandy to talk about advantages made available by technological developments, but can we sit idly by and say we will provide them to only 2 percent of the population when we know darn well that others desperately need them? And if so, what is the cost?

Finally, the problem of the impact of applying technological development to the patient himself. What does that new technological development do to the patient? I want to illustrate: In the rehabilitation field we use instruments that help perform the functions of the normal arm, for instance. We use a device that helps the patient mobilize his arms better. Well, we had a patient for whom we had spent quite a lot of time attaching one of these devices; we thought to help him achieve his personal independence in a much better way. However, after he went back home he found a solution much more satisfactory to him: He hired another person to do these basic necessities of living for him, which was much quicker and better than he could do for himself. Thus, we found that this device that we had sort of tailored for him had not even been used, and we asked him why he didn't use it. He said, "Well, very simply, I found someone else who could do these things more effectively and with less time and cost than I could do them on my own." And we said, "Why didn't you tell us?" He replied, "I didn't tell you because I thought it was very important *for you* to try that thing out on me."

We can also say that new technological development may create on the part of the patient the attitude that the personal relationship between himself and the physician will be lost, that he will be dealing more and more with anonymous instrumental agencies. And then the question arises: is this possible or not? I know this is not possible and it will not happen, but the problem exists in some persons' minds that this may lead to automatic diagnosis by the computer! There are two things here: the fact that the computer may tell us the diagnosis automatically and the question of what this can mean as far as the patient is concerned.

In an article I have written,[30] I allude to *The Death of Ivan Ilyitch* in which Tolstoi tells about a patient who was consulting a physician and the physician was saying these words: "Such and such a thing shows that you have such and such a thing in you, but if this is not confirmed according to the investigation of such and such a man, then you must suppose such and such a thing. Now if we suppose such and such a thing . . ."—he went on and on, while Ivan Ilyitch had only one question in mind: Was his case dangerous or not? But the doctor ignored his question. From a doctor's point of view, the question was idle and deserved no consideration; the only thing to do was await possibilities. We must ask: Are we to confront the live patient as this doctor confronted Ivan Ilyitch? I hope not. I cannot help but feel quite a bit of hope along these lines.

I hope too that many of us will not take the path of "absolutism" to which Dr. Fletcher alluded; this is gone and dead and buried, and I hope there will be no resuscitation. I prefer too that we not follow the path of "playing God" that he was talking about, because I feel we are not individually capable of this and we need

[30] See Carlos Vallbona, "Electronic Automation in Medicine: Its Moral Implications," *Linacre Quarterly* 28 (1961): 74.

restraints. I do thank Dr. Fletcher for suggesting the path of ethics; ethics breaks the chains of Prometheus. And yet Prometheus, who has stolen the fire of the gods, knows that he should not dare do that again.

DR. RAMSEY: Perhaps I should explain that it is not sufficient reason for me being here that I was to give Dr. Vallbona a little company as reactor. I am very happy to do so, however, because of Professor Fletcher's *Morals and Medicine,* a book which I found very stimulating. I don't know whether he would particularly approve of the result of that stimulation; I don't think so—but this is, in fact, biographically the case: that book has been an important part of my undergraduate life.

I find it rather difficult even to imagine that I can make a hopeful comment on Professor Fletcher's address; it is rather hard to take hold of a distillation of statements and phrases of technology. But, just to get over a few things: It is a little too late in this forum to persuade you that you cannot encapsulate the moral choice of men in those three alternatives of ethical analysis in which you think love and concern should be mated to technology in the human interest. That, in my opinion, is inadequate to the problem. Love and ethics will certainly never have to go on a Metrecal diet. That is to say, there is fullness and there is articulation with respect to that little judgment we do desperately need, especially in a technological age. Now, it may very well be that one or the other of those systems of ethics will not be able to survive in an age of technology, and that I frankly grant. That, however, precisely defines the grace of men in an age of technology. Ethics, which in itself is reflection, is certainly fitted and suitable to survive the age of technology; but the question of survivability in the galloping technological age would seem to me not really to be the point.

On most of the things in Professor Fletcher's remarks I find myself in entire agreement. I have really no questions to pose to him, precisely because his was simply a reflection—as I take it—upon our doing as technology enables us to do. With most of that, certainly, and with certain qualifications, I would agree. There is no ability without taking initiative, and that initiative would certainly be in line with the developments in technology. But I do want to stress the fact—and I think this is a category that needs to be opened —that Professor Fletcher did state that the taking of initiative includes the taking of initiative in order to withhold. I want to dwell upon that for just two or three sentences.

As Professor Thielicke has remarked, this age of technology would deprive a man of his right to die piece by piece.[31] We must open up not only the category of being allowed to die, but of being allowed to die by choice. If Professor Fletcher and I had long enough to talk about it, I think we would agree that there is no question, so far as religious ethics is concerned, that this is not to be equated with the category of suicide; the choice of life under certain technological traditions is within our moral ethics.

I do want to emphasize, with respect to Professor Fletcher's suggestion, that the taking of initiative includes not only somehow communicating to the patients of technological medicine the technical responsibility, but also somehow giving them psychological support in human decision of this sort. This is certainly desperately urgent.

DR. FLETCHER: Certainly, as in the case of Norbert Weiner and of others like him who have examined all of the potentials of cybernation and automation, it is important for us to recognize what I call the negative serendipity, and be realistic about this vital business of technology. It is a sharp knife which can cut both ways, thus indeed adding to our responsibilities.

I am indebted to Dr. Vallbona for the three lines of further inquiry, which I try to pursue in my own way. First of all, with respect to pursuing computer prognoses and diagnoses, what about the privacies of the patient as it has been classically conceived? Then, what about the transference of life-death decisions to machines? And, thirdly, from the point of view of social decisions, if there is conflict between the decision of the physician and the mechanical judgment of the computer—which should rule?

I am also gravely concerned, referring once more to Dr. Vallbona's comments, about the problem of selection. It is not a new problem. Technology only poses it to us in somewhat more complex and harrowing ways sometimes. But already there must of necessity exist some medical-civil authorities selection committees to deal with supply and demand in many respects, perhaps most notably in the public concept in regard to the dialysis machinery.

[31] See below, p. 163.

I am a little at a loss just now to grasp all that might be implicit in Dr. Vallbona's questions about the psychological impact of modern technological medical care on the patient. I am sure just in the very nature of things that it is a valid and maybe far more important question than I have yet fully appreciated, although we are all fairly well familiar with the negative reaction of the patient to medical care already.

I knew in advance that Professor Ramsey would say that there are more than three alternative methods of ethical analysis, and I knew that he would say that any proposal that loving concern should be wedded to technology for the human interest is inadequate to the problem. I am only disappointed that he didn't tell us why, and one of these days I'm going to find out.

And I am delighted that he has laid greater emphasis on what was implicit, but not explicit, in my remark about the matter of initiative, which really needs to be at the core of responsibility. It must work both ways; sometimes the responsibility side of initiative may be to withhold. I entirely agree with him, and I also submit that this matter, which we can illustrate in terms of many medical problems—sometimes the decision to let the patient go—needs far more investigation than it has had.

QUESTIONER: Dr. Fletcher, I think most of us accept the fact that the absolutist kind of ethics is gone; but I have some problems with the optimism about man's ability to love. If love is the measure of the ethic, what is the measure of love? Is there any historical continuity, is there any historical consistency of love, and what is the measure of it? Has man the capacity to feel and to act out loving concern? And if so, what does that mean? How does he act lovingly concerned?

DR. FLETCHER: I suppose my reaction on the first score is that men do have a limited capacity to feel and act out loving concern. Yes. And I believe there is quite a considerable body of empirical data which could be cited in support of that view. That is without prejudice, of course, to what is at stake.

On the second score, I suppose there are two ways—if we had the time—that we might go, in answering the question: What is it to act lovingly? One might be ethical, for example, in terms of the notion of summary rules or general propositions about the most constructive way to act in our neighbor's interest as based upon a wide range of experience. There are lots of generalized propositions about what is good with respect to communication, group, and so forth.

Another way to get at it might be theological—if you are in that camp, as I am. And I would see here a most fruitful model for what it means to be a loving man, that is to say, a man for others, in Jesus Christ. But I think our difficulties often arise when we turn to this—or any other—model of loving concern with the demand that this open-ended, free, responsible, and sensitive lovingness should be reduced to some prefabricated rules.

And, I think, it is on this final part of your question where perhaps the present debate in ethics is being waged most fiercely.

Part Three

THEOLOGICAL FOUNDATIONS

6. Ethics in Modern Medicine

The theological substance of the conference was provided by the German theologian and ethicist, Helmut Thielicke, who has done more work in theological ethics than any other thinker in the history of Christianity. One of the giants in the postwar theological revival in Germany, he has contributed to the ethical discussion immeasurably in his three-volume Theologische Ethik *(for the volumes thus far translated into English, see the Bibliography). He has also written and spoken widely on ethics in medicine and technology. One of the world's great preachers, his sermons are fascinating interpretations of the Christian faith in the modern idiom. He is presently Professor of Systematic Theology at the University of Hamburg in Germany.*

Dr. Thielicke's series of lectures undergirded the experience of the conference as a whole. They were basically an extended exploration of the uniqueness of man as this provides directives for concrete decision making in medical ethics. The presentation was divided into three main parts which dealt with the ambiguity of progress, organ transplants and the prolongation of life, and the future of man.

Whoever is confronted by the work of Helmut Thielicke feels that he is moving at the depths of human experience, and the conference participants were no exception in this regard. Many of the physicians present were profoundly moved by the philosophic depth of the presentations. Dr. Thielicke bears the richness of European Catholic Christianity as this has been shaped by the Reformation. His psychological and sociological insight is profound. As he lectures, one is struck by the universalism of a medieval Everyman *or Goethe's* Faust. *He speaks of the virulent opposition of nature, which, having been violated, responds to the titanic usurpation of man.*

In substance, the following pages represent the Thielicke lectures as they were delivered at the conference. We have thought it best, however, for the sake of the American reader to substitute here a completely fresh translation based on the published German version of the lectures. Except for a few transitional sentences derived from the conference tapes, the following text is therefore a direct translation of Wer Darf Leben? Der Arzt als Richter *(Tübingen: Wunderlich, 1968).*

Reactions to Professor Thielicke's lectures came from Dr. Harold Rorschach, Chairman of the Department of Physics at Rice University; Dr. Blair Justice, Assistant to the Mayor of the City of Houston; and Dr. Albert Moraczewski, Research Professor at the Institute of Religion in the Texas Medical Center. Excerpts from their remarks are included at the end of this chapter.

The Doctor as Judge of Who Shall Live and Who Shall Die

Helmut Thielicke

FUNDAMENTAL CONSIDERATIONS

The Basic Questions

Medicine has made such tremendous advances in the modern period that there seems to be almost no limit to what it can do. This very fact raises a host of fundamental questions, chief of which is probably the question concerning the nature and destiny of man himself. In the field of medicine this question becomes quite specific: Is there something about man that dare not be changed—something in his very nature that dare not be violated—if he is to remain human? And if there is this fixed and inviolable something, then to what extent dare we manipulate man? To what extent dare we implement the technical capacity of modern medicine to transform him, to change the way he functions, indeed, to alter his genetic constitution?

These questions from the field of medicine can hardly be answered without first raising much more fundamental questions: What actually constitutes that "humanity" which the physician is pledged to uphold by terms of his Hippocratic oath, and where is one to draw the line which circumscribes its limits? Is it present in what might be called the completely depersonalized biological larva, where nothing remains—nothing can be revived—except the minimal operations of the lower nervous system and the rudimentary bodily functions?[1] Is the doctor categorically obliged to preserve a life which no longer "exists" but merely "vegetates," where consciousness is gone and cannot be restored? Does the dignity of the humanum extend even to this remnant of the bios?

Since these questions have really to do with the nature of human existence, with what it means to be a man, they exceed the competence of medical people alone to decide. Indeed, they demand the concerted attention of all who in their thought, research, and practice deal with the question of human existence. To adapt a well-known saying, the humanum is too serious a matter to be entrusted exclusively to the physicians. The question is addressed also to the philosopher and theologian, and he cannot evade it, even though his contribution to the discussion must admittedly be a limited one.

I, for example, am professionally engaged with ethical questions all the time. But this does not mean that I have all the answers in a matter such as this. For one thing, I simply lack the technical competence, despite the fact that for years now I have been learning all I can on the subject through talking with people more knowledgeable than myself, and through reading their books.

But more importantly, the very nature of the borderline questions with which we are here confronted precludes the possibility of any final answers: the questions must remain open. Thus, I come to this discussion, not with cocksure answers, but as a fellow inquirer who shares the uncertainties which are common to all in this time of transition. No one who is committed to the gospel—the message of the incarnation of the eternal Word—can claim to have some kind of supratemporal knowledge (a *philosophia perennis*). He knows that he is simply one of the many who have not yet arrived but are still on the way (*theologia viatorum*).

Now this observation, that we are caught up in a particular moment of history, is significant for our particular problem. It is important for us to understand that, as regards the control and management of our enhanced knowledge and refined technical capacities, we stand indeed at a historical juncture. For those who are aware of it, the openness of the transitional situation constitutes

[1] Alfred Gütgemanns, Über ärztliche Verantwortung in der Chirurgie?" *Münchener Medizinischer Wochenschrift,* 1967, no. 7, p. 14.

an impediment to precipitate action and a warning against the over-hasty adoption of premature solutions.

And the fact is that we do live in a time of transition. Advances in man's technical and scientific capacity have outstripped, as it were, the development of man himself, so that the two are no longer "synchronized." What man "can do" is out of step with what man "is" and, as things stand now, we are simply unable to cope with the resultant tension. Nobody seems to have the solution; perhaps no one ever will. I shall attempt to delineate the contours of this tension in terms of two characteristic questions, questions which are presently open and will perhaps always remain open.

1) The first question was stated by W. Wachsmut at the 94th Congress of German Surgeons meeting in Munich: "When may we discontinue our efforts to preserve life, and when must we deliberately continue them even at the risk of preserving a mental defective?" The effort to make whole becomes absurd if it ends up in producing the very opposite of what it intended. Somewhere, therefore, the physician's mandate to heal must reach its limit. But at what point and on what basis? That is the real question. Wachsmut asks in effect: How far should one go in giving help?

To ask the question in this way, however, is to blunt the very point of it. Help is something that in the very nature of the case cannot be limited. You cannot just tell the man who lives for others that he should now suddenly cease and desist. To state the question more precisely one would have to ask instead: At what point does help cease to be help and begin to cancel itself out? Can it still be called "help" when all that remains of the patient is a physical or mental torso?[2]

Obviously, no physician can be required to utilize "all the means at his disposal" in order to prolong a life entrusted to his care.[3] But when, if at all, may the doctor quit prolonging a life? A decision on this question would seem to depend on whether the life in question can be prolonged "for a period of time which will be meaningful," that is, whether the medical effort will make it possible for the patient not merely to "vegetate" but actually to

[2] Ibid., p. 8.

[3] Rudolf Kautsky, "Fragen ärztlicher Ethik in der Neurochirurgie," *Acta Neurochirurgica* 6, no. 3 (1958): 221.

"exist" as a human being. Thus we are thrown back once again to the question: What is this specifically human existence and how can we put it into words?

Here is where the question transcends the purely medical realm of inquiry and we are forced to consider the very nature of human existence: What is man? Thus a tension arises between that which is *not* under our control, the fundamental meaning and purpose of human existence, and that which *is* under our control, namely, the marvelous ministrations of sophisticated modern medicine—the problem being that, by preserving a man only in part, medicine may actually be depriving him of, and thereby violating, the very meaning and purpose of his life. Where this tension mounts to high levels of intensity, it begins to blur the line of demarcation between healing and blasphemy.

2) Fully as important, however, as establishing the negative limits to the implementation of medicine's ever mounting capacity to manipulate is the matter of determining the positive goals to be achieved by such manipulation, for example, by hormonal and neurosurgical interventions or by altering hereditary material. This question concerning goals arises as a result of certain utopian fantasies in which some thinkers have envisioned a superculture of man's own making, one with which man himself, in his natural state, would no longer be able to cope.[4] By this I mean that in terms of native endowment man would simply lack the mental or biological capacity to deal with and control the things he has himself made, and that as a result they would slip out of his grasp. Man's limited intelligence would be outwitted by the superior intelligence of his machines—a situation analogous to that portrayed by Goethe in his *Sorcerer's Apprentice*—with results that would in no way accord with man's wishes and desires in the matter. Thus, for example, man himself might appear to be "badly engineered" and in need of restructuring. Indeed, this has actually been asserted as regards space travel; it has even been suggested that we breed astronauts without legs!

To what extent, then, should we allow for biological manipulation, and then also for alteration of hereditary material? It is shock-

[4] See, e.g., the report on the London symposium sponsored by the Ciba Foundation in Gordon E. Wolstenholme, ed., *Man and His Future: A Ciba Foundation Volume* (Boston: Little, Brown and Co., 1963).

ing even to think of the idea that instead of *man* being the measure of *things,* the *things* he has made—the structures of technology, progress, indeed the whole cultural apparatus—should come to determine the lines along which *man* himself is to be structured. But this is indeed the question: To what extent, if at all, may man bow before those superstructures of his own making which have now grown to such proportions as to tower above him? And the question must be faced, for it has in fact been posed!

This question is all the more pressing because what is at stake here involves more than simply the question of whether man "by nature" is capable of dealing with all this or must himself be left hopelessly behind while his technical successes multiply. The fact is that these superstructures do more than put man in the shade. They actually threaten him! They attack. They put him on the defensive. And their attack is such that man is forced to do something, not just in order to keep up with the situation but actually to survive.

Medicine, for example, with its tremendously enlarged capabilities, really moves in a vicious circle. Whatever it does to preserve diseased life threatens at the same time to deteriorate the hereditary mass. For example, a life may be prolonged which, if left unaided, would not have survived to maturity, but which, being enabled now to procreate, introduces into the hereditary chain its own deficiencies, thereby multiplying them. Thus it is not simply a case of man's natural capacities being outstripped by that which he has himself created. That which he has created actually turns upon him. It commits an act of aggression which further debilitates his original constitution and augments his helplessness.

This deterioration of the human genotype has found expression in a variety of macabre visions, conjured up mind you not just by wild-eyed journalists but also by sober and respected scientists. They speak of the population explosion on the one hand, and of man's defective hereditary substance on the other, and they say that the reciprocal relation between the two threatens to convert the whole world in the not too distant future into "one gigantic hospital, full of emotionally disturbed people, neurotics, mental defectives, and prosthetics cases—people who could not live except for the continuing support they receive from outside themselves [from technology]."[5] It has even been suggested that what is in the offing is a "prosthetics culture."

If you specialists will allow a layman the privilege, I can perhaps illustrate the problem by citing a concrete situation of which I have firsthand knowledge and which has set me to thinking. Statistics gathered by the Pediatrics Clinic in Hamburg indicate that of every eight thousand children born, one is phenylketonuric. This means that of the twenty thousand children born in Hamburg each year about two or three will carry this affliction. By following a rather hideous kind of diet for the rest of their lives they can nonetheless be kept alive and even be saved from the mental deficiency which would otherwise ensue. The PKU disease itself, however, is hereditary, and apart from such a strict and protracted regimen the consequences are quite predictable. Without the help of the physician the child would die before puberty. By virtue of medical intervention, however, the carrier of such hereditary material is preserved to effect a mathematically calculable increase in the incidence of the disease in later generations.

The Ambiguity of Progress

A phenomenon like this has a significant bearing on the idea of progress. Indeed, to speak of progress at all is to raise again the question as to the nature of man: What in man is constant and inviolable, and what is subject to change? This is the question that pushes beyond the limits of medical inquiry and brings other points of view into the picture.

Now, it is perfectly evident that progress is never unequivocally positive. On the contrary, it is always quite ambiguous. In the realm of the technical and physical it has long been apparent—and not just since the invention of the atomic bomb—that constructive powers are always accompanied by a destructive tendency. The situation is quite similar with respect to progress in the field of medicine. If it is true that to preserve an impaired or imperiled life and bring it to its highest possible state of development is an act of responsible medicine, fully in accord with the best in medical ethics, then it is also true that this help to the individual carries with it at the same time—if I may put it rather dramatically—an

[5] Richard Kaufmann, *Die Menschenmacher* (Frankfurt: Fischer, 1964), pp. 24-25.

attack on his posterity. The act of compassion to one generation can be an act of oppression to the next. What is productive medically can be destructive eugenically.

At this point two questions arise. The first is an ethical question, the second is metaphysical and religious. We shall consider each of them briefly.

The Ethical Question of Accepting the Consequences

Ethically, the question is this: Should we not acknowledge this ambiguity of progress and willingly accept the consequences? In particular, should we not willingly pay the price that must be paid for such "productivity"?

But what precisely is this price? Surely it cannot mean that we simply give to progress a blank check whereby it can henceforth move ahead automatically and without restraint, while we try to console ourselves in the thought that the increasing pollution of our hereditary stream has at least preserved intact the infinite value of the individual human being—and while we resolve accordingly to extend and intensify our therapeutic patchwork on the individuals born later with the same affliction. To take this position is to succumb to a highly dubious inconsistency, which I can best illustrate —if you will allow—by means of a theological reflection.

In the command given with creation man was commissioned to subdue the earth. This commission clearly does not mean to let nature just take its course. Man is not simply to accept nature passively as it is. On the contrary, he is, as it were, to set himself apart from nature and regard nature as raw material which he must himself shape in a responsible way. Wherever men clear and cultivate the land, or build cultures and civilizations—or practice medicine— there is always at work this motif of intolerance over against nature. Indeed, this is true even where the opposition to nature is waged by way of instruments that must themselves be extracted from nature. Now, this whole business of creative opposition to nature is of a piece. It is not segmented. To put it in more general terms, culture building is a single indivisible process.

What this means in the case of PKU mental disease, for example, is that in effecting responsible change in natural processes it is quite impossible to intervene at only one point, and then at a second point to hold back and do nothing about the resulting disruption of the hereditary stream. Theologically speaking, this would clearly be to violate the command of creation. You cannot initiate an intervention and then just sit back and let whatever happens happen—on the ground that it has now become part of some inviolable thing called "nature." The inconsistency of such an approach is obvious.

Thus, when we speak of the "consequences" to be taken into account, the "price" to be willingly paid, we surely do not mean letting nature make of the intervention what it will. It is rather a question of willingly assuming the further responsibility of intervening once again. But this "second intervention," as I hope to demonstrate later, cannot consist merely of piecemeal therapeutic patchwork. It must rather involve preventive measures instituted on a systematic basis—specifically, eugenic measures. In the case under discussion this would probably mean sterilization.

Ethical questions of this sort, however, can never be solved merely by handing down decrees. Imposed solutions are notoriously antiethical because they make of man a mere object. If such dehumanization is to be avoided, the people who have a responsible share in determining the fate of this child—indeed the child itself once it has grown up—must be brought to understand the need for sterilization. They must be helped to see and accept the fact that life in this instance has its price. If the child is to live, it will have to forego the possibility of ever having any children of its own. The people involved must be helped to the point where they can willingly affirm that as far as they are concerned whatever "must" be—objectively and even legally—also "ought" to be.

If this is to happen there will have to be collaboration and co-operation on the part of a variety of people: parents, physicians, educators, spiritual counselors. The very diversity of the group reflects the fact that problems of this sort impinge upon many dimensions of life.[6] The fact that they also transcend the competence of any single profession is simply one more sign of their importance.

It is particularly clear in the field of medicine that interventions into nature, though commanded and apparently divinely willed, are not unequivocally positive in their results. There is a price to be paid for them. Because of their ambiguity, they must be followed

[6] On this point see the illuminating article by E. Kern, "Chirurgie und Psyche," *Therapeutische Umschau,* 1966, no. 6, pp. 256 ff.

up by a whole chain of subsequent interventions designed to prevent certain developments from occurring. Physicians are only too familiar with specific illustrations of this problem.

By way of contrast, one could also mention the fact that whoever *rejects* a particular intervention will have to pay for that too, in a readiness for undertaking other interventions. For example, the rejection of abortion places an ever greater premium on birth control.

The Religious Question Concerning the Disturbed State of the Creation

Besides this ethical question, which roots in the ambiguity of progress and the need for balancing the accounts, there arises a second question: the metaphysical and religious question which has to do with the problem of the origin of this ambiguity. If the borderline questions to which we have here referred point—almost like geometric loci—to the background of human existence, to what it was and is, then we have no alternative but to inquire into the origin of this fateful ambiguity. For the ambiguity doubtless has to do with what man is and with the fact that he has had a history.

The Christian tradition has always been aware of the mystery which here comes to light. It has seen in this ambiguity a manifestation of the halflight between creation and fall, between man as he was meant to be and as he presently is, standing in sinful contradiction to his intended destiny. With your permission, I should like to develop this thought briefly with a view to the problems which are our special concern.

In suggesting that here the ancient tale of creation and fall enters the picture, what I mean is this: The biblical account of the fall makes the point that man has placed himself in sinful contradiction to the destiny for which he was created. When he eats the forbidden fruit in order to know good and evil—you are all familiar with this venerable parable—what he is after is to be not simply like unto God in image, but equal to God in rank. As a usurper he goes beyond the bounds of his human sphere and perverts the relation between creator and creature. There are countless analogies in mythology, from the Tower of Babel to the story of Prometheus and the many varieties of titanism, which point to some similar fateful experience in the very background of human existence—an experience which is always there as the perennial starting point and which continues to determine the ongoing course of human existence. The result is that inherent in all of man's divinely-intended creativity—for example, in his productive interventions in nature—there is always that usurping quality whereby he inevitably transgresses the bounds of his creatureliness.

The story of Cain and Abel says something about the background of this ambiguity of human creativity. It tells how Cain, after killing his brother, is banished to the land of Nod—that is, the land of "Nowhere," a kind of negative utopia. There he builds a city. His descendants become miners. Included among them are also representatives of the arts, musicians who "play the lyre and pipe." Cain's family is indeed creative! But notice, the closer we come to the tapestry of human culture, the clearer becomes that red thread which runs straight through the host of figures like a twitching, bleeding artery: Mother Earth, on whose bosom the greatest men have walked, built cities, erected monuments and cathedrals, cleared primeval forests, tamed the wild elements and fought against disease—remember how the chorus in Sophocles' *Antigone* sings the praise of man—Mother Earth has also tasted and swallowed the blood of Abel. And now this blood of the murder victim crops up everywhere in drops and rivulets. Cain, the "big brother," ancestor of all humanity, makes himself felt as an enigmatic presence. Somewhere in every symphony there sounds the note of death and suffering; somewhere in every Doric pillar the sign of Cain appears; and in every tragedy there is the mournful lament over injustice and fate. Are not the miserable slaves and dispossessed, the squalid helots and peasants, indeed an integral part of the grandeur and Apollonian brilliance of Greek art? Do we who have heard the story of Cain need Marxism to tell us that? Is it really true, as Treitschke once dared to say, that a single statue of Phidias more than compensates for the squalor of millions of slaves in antiquity? Who is right: Treitschke or this biblical text?

There is an ambiguity, I say, about man's creativity. It was imposed upon him as a task at creation, yet involves at the same time a blasphemous denial of his creatureliness. It smacks both of humility and of hubris at one and the same time. And it is because of this ambiguity that art of every kind sounds the cry for release from Nod, the land of Cain's exile. Indeed, this is why every work of art which has been wrested from the constraints of reality is, as Gottfried Benn has put it, like an oasis laboriously erected in the deadly desert.

In myth—and here Attic tragedy affords a good example—this world which is no longer whole tends to be regarded as something given, an intact structure in which guilt and fate are inseparably interwoven. The Bible, on the contrary, looks instead at man. It sees not the structure, but this personal representative of our disjointed world. For this reason, when the events triggered by this basic ambiguity lead on automatically, as it were, to still other events, I can no longer get off the hook by saying, "Such is war" or "Such is life" or "That's the way it is in this old world."

Jacob Burckhardt spoke in this fashion about the "law of power." For him, the very possession of power necessarily leads to violent self-assertion, territorial aggrandizement, and continuing expansion, as if by a kind of inevitable compulsion. The biblical view of the matter is quite different. It impels me to admit that it is *I myself* who am out of order, and that, because of *my* fundamental disorder I have caused things to go the way they have. Thus we would have to assert, in opposition to Burckhardt, that it is not a case of man's being led astray by some mythical being called "power." It is rather man himself, the one who holds and exercises the power, who is here called in question. The problem is whether man is capable of dealing with that which is at his disposal.[7] Instead of speaking about some general malaise in the structure of the world into which I have somehow been innocently dragged, it is necessary to speak of *my* conflicts (and then probably also of my need for salvation!).

We can perhaps use an example from the field of atomic physics to illustrate this point, that that before which we shudder and shrink is we ourselves, and that that which causes us forever to be taking new measures and countermeasures is not any formal consequences of our action but this ambiguity in the very background of our existence. I have occasionally told people who express a fear of the atomic bomb that such fear rests on an illusion. It is not the atomic bomb as such which frightens us, but the fact that the power of the atom has fallen into the hands of man. It is

[7] See Jacob Burckhardt, *Force and Freedom: Reflections on History,* ed. James Hastings Nichols (New York: Pantheon, 1943), pp. 115 ff.

because we know about the ambiguity of man and about the damaged state of his existence that we are frightened by the increase of atomic power. For what is thereby augmented is not only the creative and constructive capability of man but also his tendency to destructive titanism. In fact, our fear of atomic power is merely a symbolic expression of what in truth could be called our fear of the abysmal possibilities of man.

For the fun of it, I have occasionally added at this point, "If the atomic bomb were to be safely stored away in a nunnery or deaconess house, it would be as harmless as a blooming cactus on the window sill." This brief aside had a truly comic aftermath one day. I had no more than finished lecturing when a dark figure, obviously in religious garb, strode briskly toward the podium. I suspected that someone might have taken offense at my mentioning the nunnery. Still, I could see no reason for alarm inasmuch as I had remained ecumenically neutral by mentioning the deaconess house as well. Imagine my surprise then at hearing this impassioned comment: "When you speak about neutralizing the threat of the atomic bomb by storing it in a nunnery or a deaconess house it is obvious that you have never lived in such a place yourself!"

Actually, this little episode illustrated in a satirical way the very thought I had been trying to express. As far as the atomic bomb is concerned, what man is really afraid of is what he sees in himself. It is simply an evasive kind of cover-up when he points the finger instead at the structure of the world, or the demonism of technology, or the ambiguity of progress—or the vicious circle implicit in every medical advance.

It is not enough, it seems to me, simply to go on repeating the obvious, that the questions in this area spill over into the fields of philosophy and theology as well as medicine. It becomes necessary at some time to say for once what this fact actually means, and to specify with precision the problems which are here opened up in unending succession.

It goes without saying—and to be fair about it I must point this out—that the non-Christian can interpret the ambiguity of the world, and hence also that phenomenon which we have here called the ambiguity of medical activity, in a very different way. In the world of Greek tragedy, for example, we obviously find models of interpretation which clearly depart from the Christian conception.

My only concern here is that, whatever the method of interpretation, we become consciously *aware* of the ambiguity. For only by such awareness are we immunized against the shallow utopias being dreamed up today by numerous apostles of biology. These people, some of them rather prominent men, hope that the current breathtaking developments in genetics will make it possible to breed man anew, along the lines indicated by the superstructures he has himself created. Whatever our philosophical orientation, our continuing awareness of the ambiguity of man is more important than our particular understanding and interpretation of it.

In our hopes for the future we must avoid unspeakable shallowness and thoughtless superficiality, and this is not easy to do, even for the most brilliant minds in biology. It is amazing how often superior intelligence and incredible banality are conjoined in the same individual. The man who believes in "easy solutions" readily falls victim to ideological fantasy and doctrinaire fanaticism. The easy solutions which lightly skip over basic conflicts will have to be paid for eventually. They presuppose a world in which the good—hence also the act of healing—can be had without price, without having to pay for it, a world in which there are no conflicts and man does not stand in contradiction to himself. And as the mystery of human existence was overlooked at the very beginning, so it is also touched up beyond recognition in the eschatological fantasies dreamed up by some biologists today. Because of the false starting point, they end up in the illusion that continuing progress in biology will eventually do away with the basic conflict of human existence, the conflict between will and instinct, spirit and flesh. They think to accomplish this either through eliminating the negative drives, for example, the aggressive instinct, neurosurgically or through paralyzing the corrosive powers by means of psychic drugs such as Huxley's "messengers of happiness," or perhaps even through genetic manipulation.

Over against this illusion we are taught by the cumulative experience of men everywhere that saints, heroes, and conquerors, people who at one time or another have come to be looked up to by their fellow men, have all grown strong in the stress of conflict and struggle. Even the peace of God is not something one quietly possesses but something toward which one restlessly strives. However construed in its many variations, the model of humanity which calls forth the universal cry of admiration, "Behold, what a man!" is hardly something that could be produced by genetic manipulation, biochemistry, or breeding. The macabre apocalyptic vision of a "mass of happy lemurs, obedient, devoid of will, directed by drugs and electrical currents"[8] is deceptive. The very naivete of such pronouncements betrays the incredible shallowness of their views of man. Here, if anywhere, is clear proof of the fact that one cannot undertake to make even biological or medical judgments unless one is also willing to face up to certain fundamental decisions and bring within the focus of his scholarly concern the very nature of human existence.

SPECIFIC PRACTICAL PROBLEMS

We have spoken of the limits and the goals of medical science, and of the basic ambiguity of progress—which is quite apparent, for example, in the case of PKU mental disease—and we have said that the reasons for this ambiguity lie in the religious realm. The Christian tradition from the very beginning has always linked a progressive civilization with the fact that man is God's perverted creature. These broad reflections on the basic nature of man grew inevitably out of our general survey of the problems before us.

We are also concerned, however, with some pressing practical problems which concretely illustrate these more general questions. You will, of course, neither expect nor allow me to detail here the host of medical-ethical problems with which we are presently confronted. Even if I were qualified to do this, a case-by-case rehearsal would hardly allow for more than the briefest comment. Moreover, it would be the height of presumption for a nonspecialist like myself summarily to judge every sort of medical action.

Instead I have decided to select certain models of medical activity which illustrate well the questions posed for us by this time of transition in which we live. I have in mind two particular problems, those having to do with the limits of artificially prolonging life, and those having to do with the question of organ transplants. Later on, when we come to explore these matters further with reference to the nature of man, I hope to comment also on the matter of interventions in genetics.

[8] Kaufmann, *op. cit.*, p. 129.

The Artificial Prolongation of Life

On November 24, 1957, in receiving an International Congress of Anesthesiologists, Pope Pius XII made some carefully considered pronouncements regarding the problem of resuscitation and the artificial prolongation of life. Among other things, he said that the rights and duties of a family called to make a decision in these matters "depend in general upon the presumed will of the unconscious patient if he is of age and '*sui juris*.' Where the proper and independent duty of the family is concerned, they are usually bound only to the use of ordinary means."[9] What this apparently means is that the family is not obligated to press for the extraordinary measures which today are within the province of progressive medicine, measures which can sometimes preserve certain vital functions even when they cannot preserve the organism as a whole, including its capacity for self-consciousness and self-control.

The pope states further, "If it appears that the attempt at resuscitation constitutes in reality such a burden for the family that one cannot in all conscience impose it upon them, they can lawfully insist that the doctor should discontinue these attempts, and the doctor can lawfully comply."[10] Thus the doctor, for example, can "remove the artificial respiration apparatus before the blood circulation has come to a complete stop."[11] If I interpret this properly, the "burden" which one dare not impose on the "conscience" of the relatives does not refer primarily to the financial or other demands upon them which may become too great. In all likelihood what the pope has in mind is rather the emotional strain. How does one maintain a human and loving concern for a being which is no longer a person but merely the empty shell of what once was human, a being with which communication is nonexistent and which can therefore no longer act as an independent subject but only play the inhuman role of an object?

[9] "The Artificial Prolongation of Life: An Address of Pope Pius XII to an International Congress of Anesthesiologists, November 24, 1957," *The Pope Speaks* 4, no. 4 (Spring 1958): 397. See also "Anesthesia—Three Moral Questions: An Address of Pope Pius XII to a Symposium of the Italian Society of Anesthesiology, February 24, 1957," *The Pope Speaks* 4, no. 1 (Summer 1957): 33-49.

[10] Ibid.

[11] Ibid.

Implicit in what the pope has said here is a certain view of man. If we investigate his statement with reference to its anthropological content, two main points of view seem to emerge.

The Distinction between Human Life and Biological Life

When we speak of the duty of the physician to preserve life we surely must be referring not to biological life as such but only to "human" life, a life which can hardly be characterized in terms of the factors measured by electrocardiograms and electroencephalograms but for which other criteria are needed. From Genesis to Heidegger—if one may rashly cover so broad a sweep in a single overview—the crucial criterion for differentiating between animal life and human life is the human consciousness of self. I may suggest very briefly what this means.

In the biblical narrative of creation, the creatures—stars, plants, and animals—are only objects of the creative "Let there be!" Man, on the contrary, is addressed in the second person as "you." He is entrusted with a commission to be fulfilled, a destiny to be realized, and with reference to these it is indeed possible for him to fail. Thus man is called into a partnership with the creator, and to this call he must respond. Because man has to become what he was intended to be, he is—in the words of Sartre—"condemned to freedom." Accordingly, as the story of the fall shows, man is forbidden to abandon his role as subject. He is forbidden to conceive of himself as one who is innocently betrayed, led astray, determined by a chain of cause and effect. Any such attempt to turn guilt into fate is here nipped in the bud.

In this same way Heidegger distinguishes human existence from all other being by the fact that it involves a consciousness of self, a laying hold of one's own being. This consciousness of self has reference particularly to knowledge about what lies ahead, and hence also to knowledge about death. Man's anxiety and hope have reference to the future, whereas the animal, not having a consciousness of self, remains a prisoner of the present moment.

Consciousness of self is thus the critical sign of human existence. Only because of self-consciousness does suffering, for example, have any meaning. For connected with the gift of self-consciousness is the duty—and also the possibility—of "reacting" to suffering. We react whether we combat it or accept it, whether we give up in the face of suffering or let it become the crucible that tempers and strengthens us, whether we resist to the point of nullifying it or proceed to integrate it into our life. Thus, for man suffering can be an ethical act; it can even become a positive duty. For the animal, by contrast, suffering is nothing but a burden to be done away as quickly as possible; we end it mercifully with a bullet through the head. To end man's suffering in this way would be a crime—because the bullet would destroy all possibility of a meaningful existence. Only what is notoriously without meaning can be abandoned to destruction.

If we take seriously the fact that consciousness of self is the characteristic sign of human existence, then the complete and irreparable loss of this consciousness would indicate that human existence is no longer there. A man devoid of any trace of self-consciousness would be, as it were, merely a biological culture. One could possibly wish to keep "it" alive, for example, as a source of organs for transplant operations, but hardly for reasons of medical ethics.

Now, it appears—even to me—as if in making these broad generalizations I am skirting a vast array of deep and difficult questions. For example, one need not look very far ahead to see looming up the immediate and unsettling question of whether we even dare to speak of consciousness of self in such general terms. Are we not obliged rather to introduce at once a quantitative point of view and ask about various degrees of consciousness? Beyond what lower limit would the traces of consciousness have become so minute as to justify our saying that no life remains?

Here too, in asking these questions, I do not have in mind any physically observable indices for such traces of consciousness, factors which could be registered on our apparatuses. What I have in mind is rather the way in which the consciousness of self finds expression in communication, whereby traces of the subject-self may possibly be manifest in interpersonal contact, for example, in the fact that the patient is susceptible of being addressed. I believe it would be wrong to assess these traces in terms of rational criteria. I remember what Bodelschwingh said about his dealings with seriously deranged persons (and he had extensive experience in these matters). He thought he sometimes detected a response to various acts of love, perhaps even to a hymn or a word of Scripture. I myself would not dare to dispute this sign of humanity even in one whose consciousness of self no longer finds expression in articulated words but moves—as perhaps in the case of the schizophrenic—in dimensions beyond our hermeneutical grasp. It is conceivable that a person who is dying may stand in a passageway where human communication has long since been left behind, but which nonetheless contains a self-consciousness different from any other of which we know. For this reason that lower limit which divides human existence from a biological culture must probably be nothing less than the total absence of all self-consciousness.

The Doctor and "Metaphysical Guilt"

In connection with this same papal pronouncement I would like to advance yet another perspective. Even where the consciousness of self is dimmed almost to extinction, it is still questionable whether a life which is surely expiring should be maintained in a flickering state and not be allowed to go out. I concede, to be sure, that it is extremely difficult to provide a good argument for this. It is certainly impossible to provide casuistic criteria for the conduct of the physician. Perhaps what expresses itself here is simply an instinct about what ought to be, an instinct which first exists and then awkwardly casts about for ex post facto arguments to justify its existence. Having openly conceded this possibility, I may perhaps be permitted to speak further of the matter.

1) "It is appointed for men to die once" (Heb. 9:27). This apparently means also that man has a right to die. Is it permissible to take his death away from him piece by piece when his hour has obviously come? The nature of my present argument is such that at this point I can do no more than raise the question.

2) The thrust of this question, however, is enhanced by the further reflection that such piecemeal prolongation of the process of dying results in an absurd situation in which the prolongation of life is turned into a prolongation of agony. Equally absurd is the resulting disproportion between the life of the person here in process of dying, and the fragmentary life functions which are being artificially prolonged. It is possible that the physician who in these borderline territories works to maintain life at all costs will

find that he has been shoved out into a no man's land in which vocation or calling impinges in an alarming manner upon vice or crime.

Yes, crime! Is not the doctor confronted by the question of whether in his action he is trying to prevent what nature intends—or what God intends? Is he not seeking a Pyrrhic victory when he tries to hold death—at least in part—at bay for days or even hours? Whatever man is intended to be—and we have already shown that human destiny is also a concern of the physician—he is doubtless supposed to be that in point of time. That is to say, his destiny is to be realized within the framework of human finitude, within the limits of temporal existence. To that extent, of course, death is something to be affirmed. Am I permitted then to delay it at all costs?

Once again I discover that I am beginning to ask questions. Argumentation tends to take the form of questioning the moment we tackle the borderline problems—problems which cannot be resolved by casuistic definitions but demand that we venture to make decisions. We should have known, however, that there are these borderline territories; there are regions in which modern medical know-how threatens to turn the physician's task of healing men into the inhuman crime of terrorizing them.

In these areas there are no easy solutions. Whichever way we turn, we come up against borders which give us no peace. Indeed, they impose upon us a heavy burden of guilt—not a juridical or even a moral guilt but a feeling of "metaphysical guilt" which calls us into question in an existential way.

I speak of "metaphysical" guilt because here there is no alternative course—as there is in respect to moral decisions—whereby I could avoid this kind of guilt. It is not a case of my choosing a particular evil in the place of some unambiguous good I might otherwise have chosen. The basis of guilt does not reside in the particular character of my action—and the fact that I could have acted differently—but in the very structure of my human existence. It is a matter of being, not action. I am here confronted by a fundamentally insoluble conflict—insoluble because it is rooted in my very nature. Because I cannot escape from myself, I cannot escape this conflict either. It is this nonobjectifiable existential guilt which finds expression in Greek tragedy, as well as in the Christian doctrine of original sin.

How is it that this conflict, which manifests itself precisely in the situation of the physician, is rooted in our very existence and hence is connected with a feeling of "metaphysical guilt"? I have already pointed out that the action of the physician, like all cultural activity, is an intervention in nature. The commission given to man at creation says that man is not simply to accept passively whatever existence may come to him "by nature." He is rather to wrest his existence from nature, and in opposing her attain his destiny. On the other hand, our destiny is not realized exclusively in the protest against the will of nature, for it is also possible that nature herself apportions or decrees something for us. In other words, it is possible that, in part, nature makes us what we are to be. Pain and suffering make this rather apparent.

Thus, on the one hand, it surely is part of man's nature to combat suffering, and in this respect to protest against the natural processes which impose this suffering upon us. Not only medicine but all socially constructive efforts to improve the world have their genesis in our disposition to rise up against rapacious meaninglessness, against pain and suffering, and in the name of meaning in human life to protest.

On the other hand, we are also confronted by the fact that this suffering could be ordained for us. It could be part and parcel of our very destiny. What would humanity be if suffering were to be totally eliminated and we knew nothing but the absurd happiness of dull lemurs? It is hardly necessary for me to remind you of that which each one of us owes to what he has suffered in life, and of how many people go to pieces because they have been denied this burden of purification. Thus, even suffering can be "ordained," however much the physician may—and in terms of his commission must—use the tools of nature to oppose nature's aggressions.

But which of the two alternatives is incumbent upon us in any given instance? Are we to oppose the aggression of diseased nature to the bitter end, using the most refined methods available to modern medicine? Or are we rather to accept suffering? Are we—and I do not mean this in any pious devotional sense—are we to submit humbly to our lot?

Here I am confronted with a conflict as to how I shall realize my human destiny. I am caught up in a conflict between that which I take to be my duty as a physician—to act against the aggression of nature—and that which, precisely in this aggression, comes through to me as a call to realize my destiny as a human being. And no man—really, no man!—is able to decide this alternative: whether to realize our destiny in a thoroughgoing and technically professional resistance to the fate decreed by nature, or whether to realize it instead precisely in the acceptance of that which purifies us. For pain exercises not only a negative function in our life but also a creative function whereby it helps us to become what we are supposed to be.

When we find ourselves caught up in this insoluble conflict we normally take recourse to doing "whatever is medically possible," and then understanding the rest—whatever lies beyond our powers—as something over which we have no control. Either we grit our teeth and accept it fatalistically, or else we peacefully "submit ourselves to the will of God." However questionable this approach, pragmatically it may still be the best solution. It no longer suffices, however, when the physician finds himself in that borderline situation of which we have been speaking, where he is confronted with the question of whether he will attempt to prolong at all costs a life that is clearly dying, a biological life devoid of self-consciousness. I should like simply to ask: Is the physician really being true to his calling in such a case when in doctrinaire fashion he makes life an absolute? Might not such presumed vocational faithfulness be rather a matter of rebellion against the destiny now intended for this patient, and against the limit which has been set upon the physician's art?

Because of the particular character of the basic conflict, there are in this sphere no casuistic rules to tell one what to do. One must simply run the risk of making the decision—and be prepared in so doing to err, and thereby to incur guilt. As a Christian, I would say that whoever hopes to come through it all without illusions or repressions will have to live in the name of forgiveness.

The Transplantation of Organs

Having reached the point in our consideration of these profound and weighty matters where medicine comes smack up against theology, we raised some truly "ultimate" questions. I should like now to turn to more concrete problems, though these too may open the way to further discussion of anthropological questions.

The Problem of the Doctor

In dealing with my announced theme of organ transplants[12] my concern will not be with the many legal problems involved, even though these, as K. H. Bauer has shown,[13] involve an equally large number of ethical questions, for example, in the area of the relation between donor and recipient. I shall limit myself to dealing with but a few questions, which again may serve as illustrative. I shall be concerned specifically with the replacement of vital organs, whether by machines such as the electrical pacemaker and the artificial kidney, or by human organs from either living or dead donors.

The replacement of organs by machines or by the organs of other persons raises again the question as to the nature of man, though this time in somewhat different terms. Is man to be understood in analogy to the machine, whose parts are exchangeable? It is important here to note carefully the precise terms of the question. We are not asking—as certain architects of a biological utopia ask—whether man himself is to be exchanged and restructured; we are asking only whether certain parts or aspects of man can or should be exchanged.

The very formulation of the question points to the presupposition that there is something constant in man—an entelechy of indelible character—which is itself not exchangeable. What this means, of course, is that the intention is not to alter the structure of personality by, for example, manipulating or exchanging the brain. Interventions in the functioning of the brain are undertaken not in order to change the man, but in order to free him from pain or danger—though in certain circumstances the procedure may entail the risk of some change of personality. It goes without saying that there is a fundamental difference between inflicting evil as a matter of intention and accepting it as a matter of risk, as a possible but unintentional by-product of therapeutic endeavor. This decisive

---

[12] On this whole question see the documents of the Ciba Foundation Symposium entitled, *Ethics in Medical Progress: With Special Reference to Transplantation*, ed. Gordon E. Wolstenholme and Maeve O'Connor (Boston: Little, Brown and Co., 1966), esp. pp. 139-70. See also Felix Largiader, ed., *Organtransplantation* (Stuttgart: Thieme, 1966), particularly the section on "Wahrung der Wurde des sterbenden Patienten," pp. 82 ff.

[13] See K. H. Bauer, "Über Rechtsfragen bei homologer Organtransplantation in der Sicht des Klinikers," *Der Chirurg*, 1967, no. 6, pp. 245 ff.

ethical distinction is one with which we have long been familiar in the field of medicine as a result of experiences quite unrelated to transplants. It plays a role, for instance, in the question of euthanasia. While a physician under no circumstances may intend to kill, it is possible in connection with other therapeutic or pain-relieving measures for him to accept the risk of death, or of hastening its arrival.

The ethical question concerning organ transplants is in the first place, then, a question concerning purpose: To what end is the transplant undertaken? What is the goal intended? In this connection we can disregard the utopian goal to which we have already referred. Here the intention is to restructure man, to accommodate him—or certain of his organs—to the technical possibilities he has himself created, for example, to breed astronauts without legs because legs constitute a handicap in a space capsule (we may forego mentioning any of the other wild suggestions of this nature that have been put forward).

If we keep our feet on the ground we will regard organ transplants or organ replacements simply as ways of maintaining the life of the patient, limiting his suffering, and providing for him the possibility of a meaningful life. On such a view, the replacement of a heart or a kidney falls clearly within the framework of the age-old responsibility of the physician to heal. If we disregard the complicated questions of detail, including those from the sphere of law, it is difficult to see that any limit should be set to what is permissible—always assuming of course that the identity of man is respected, not changed in the name of pragmatic aims.

The Problem of Society

The real ethical questions arise, not in connection with what the doctor does, but at the point where his activity opens up certain questions for society. The ethical problem exists for the physician too, but only insofar as he has to act in the name of society. Society stands here in a situation of moral stress because for financial reasons—and indeed many other reasons as well—it is not able to help all but only a select and limited number of those needing help.

For example, as long as the obstacle of the rejection mechanism has not been surmounted, we have to continue to depend on the artificial kidney. Here then—to speak of but one aspect of the ethical problem—the question of cost arises. In my country alone, to care for our fifteen hundred kidney patients each year would require an annual outlay of half a billion marks. Can we afford to spend that amount? Even in the wealthy United States only a fraction of the needy patients can be treated. Would we not have to deny ourselves all the comforts of civilization, and possibly even cut back on certain essential social services, in order to do justice to the basic command to save life? If we were to accord to human life in fact the dignity we customarily ascribe to it in theory, would we not have to give this most elemental claim priority over all the other obligations of society? This is the social-ethical question which weighs heaviest on everybody concerned.

When we think the question through we make a strange discovery: We cannot simply weigh the preservation of life against everything else. Even if we consider human life to have ultimate value, so that—in the sense of Kant—human existence can never be a means to an end but only an end in itself, even then, the sacrifice or surrendering of life is repeatedly demanded, and not just in time of war. Without attempting to explore the many ramifications of the questions which arise here, I should simply like to call attention to one decisive aspect.

Even where human life is at stake, we repeatedly come up against the fact of incommensurability, which prevents our establishing exact degrees of priority. This came home to me again in a new way as we attempted to rebuild our nation following World War II. Here too nobody suggested that we must first cope with the problems of housing, food, and clothing—the basic necessities of life—before we started pottering around with theater props, cranking out movies, and building churches and museums. Civilized society, it would appear, forms an indivisible whole. It cannot be functionally divided in the sense of distinguishing between the basic necessities of life on the one hand and the cultural or leisure-time superstructure on the other, the former alone having absolute preeminence. If we were to proceed in this fashion, would we ever get beyond the bare walls and arrive at any kind of embellishment or beautification of life? The parts of the cultural corpus are apparently related to one another like communicating vessels: they are interrelated and reciprocally affect one another—in any case, they cannot be separated from one another. And when I say this, I do not mean this is the way it ought to be; I mean this is the way it is. For this reason, intensive preoccupation with the elemental sphere of life—as after a catastrophe—can have no absolute, but only a symbolic significance.

The case seems quite similar with respect to the problem of artificial kidneys. There has apparently been no decision to devote our entire substance—over and above what is needed for the basic necessities—to this one task of prolonging life.

But then there immediately arises the burden of a new ethical problem, the question of selection, which "would elevate the physician to the position of king and judge."[14] And here the most immediately pressing matter is that of the technical questions: Who is to make the decision concerning life and death? And according to what criteria is this decision to be made?

With this last question, though, we have again transcended the dimension of the technical and stand once more before the mystery of the humanum itself. And is it not this mystery which renders absurd every distinction we might draw between the life which is allowed to perish and the life which is earmarked for saving? To distinguish between them is indeed absurd, and for a very simple reason.

In order to be able to choose between two human beings I must have criteria for making the necessary judgment, and these must of course be obvious, objective, commonly accepted criteria. But what criteria are there, other than the purely pragmatic, on which to base such a decision? We can do no more, for example, than ask: Which among the possible candidates for an artificial kidney would be a "more valuable member of society"? Or, who has the best chance to live? Or, who shows the greatest promise of a successful and fulfilled life in the broadest sense? But where does it get us when we ask questions of this sort? Do we not thereby do violence to the incommensurable, incalculable worth of human life, which we customarily say has unconditional value as an end in itself? That which is unconditional has about it a quality that is

[14] P. H. Rossier, Éthique medicale et transplantation renale," *Urologia internationalis* (Basel) 21 (1966): 141-46.

not subject to quantitative criteria. We can never speak of that which is unconditional in terms of more or less. The criterion of the quantitative applies only in the realm of the pragmatic. Here it is indeed proper to speak of something being more worthy or less worthy, more functional or less functional. But, once this criterion is accepted, have we not opened ourselves to that horrible tendency which leads finally to the concept of the life which is not fit to live and must be liquidated?

Thus, the problem of the artificial kidney drives us to a consideration of fundamental questions whose scope and depth are almost beyond reckoning. For one thing, it confronts us inescapably with a basic either/or, which must be faced sooner or later by anyone who would seriously consider the nature of man. I might describe this alternative as follows.

The Question of Selection

One possibility is to understand the value and dignity of man in terms of his "utility," for example, his capacity to function in the productive process, or his biological or historical potential. If I do this, I can recognize, respect, and regard him according to his accomplishments. On such a view, I can even use the slogan which Stalin used and speak of "positive humanism." But then I am also compelled to take into account that which cannot be given this mark of excellence, that which is not "useful" or no longer "useful." Not because I have criminal, sadistic, or destructive inclinations, but because of my pragmatic premises, I have to recognize the presence of life that is unproductive. The pragmatic character of my criteria force me to surrender this life to destruction, to junk it as one would junk a machine which is no longer usable.

This, then, is one possibility, and a person has to be aware of what he is doing if he subscribes to it. The physician, for example, has to realize that in adopting this view of man he surrenders his healing ethos and becomes an engineer, a technician doing manipulations for a productive society. He likewise opts for the many consequences this could entail. During the Third Reich, for example, it was called "negative psychiatry" when the mentally deranged were done to death.

There is an alternative, however, to this view of man in terms of his "utility." One can speak instead of his "infinite worth," a worth over which I have no control. And here I must say quite openly that I know of no place in the world where the inviolability of man is so expressly attested and defended as in the Bible. That which from a human standpoint is valuable and useful is here radically relativized: "The last will be first and the first last." The basis of human dignity is seen to reside not in any immanent quality of man whatsoever, but in the fact that God created him. Man is the apple of God's eye. He is "dear" because he has been bought with a price: Christ died for him. Thus man stands under the patronage of an eternal benevolence and is sacrosanct. Whoever touches man has to do with God himself. The Christian tradition has had a special term for referring to this. Instead of speaking of man's own dignity it has spoken of his "alien dignity" (*dignitas aliena*), a dignity which is imparted to him and which therefore partakes of the majesty of Him who bestows it. It was in the name of this alien dignity that Bodelschwingh opposed the thugs of Hitler's SS when they sought to destroy people deemed unfit to live. Even the most pitiful life still shares in the protection of this alien dignity.

This is what I had in mind when I spoke a moment ago about the error of trying to find some kind of "objective criteria" for deciding the question of life or death in the matter of the artificial kidney. Whoever seeks for such criteria, by that very fact—though perhaps without his even knowing it—has already surrendered to the utilitarian point of view. He has attempted to apply quantitative standards to that which, because it bears the quality of the unconditional, simply cannot be measured. And in so doing he has missed the very point of the humanum, the alien dignity.

But what then are we to do? Are we, because of the threat inherent in this horrible tendency, to do nothing at all? Are we to forego the possibility of saving even the few? One only has to articulate the proposition to see how erroneous this too would be. Are we then pinned down in the no man's land between two absurdities so that, either way, the thing does not add up?

The fact is that in the borderline situation we are confronted again and again with that which indeed does not add up. Every decision is inconclusive. Here what is required above all is a recognition of this fact, so that we steer clear of the illusion of some easy solution. I shudder sometimes at the ostrich policy of many Americans, particularly at the optimism of certain physicians who, when they are pressed to make decisions which are really beyond them, try to extricate themselves from the dilemma by means of an incredibly naive argument. They say, "With the artificial kidney we condemn no one to death; we merely win life for some."

In the face of such naive optimism our very first task, it seems to me, is to confront the dilemma head on and clearly affirm the impasse. That is to say, we must enter into the suffering inherent in this situation.

One thing, however, is certain: Whoever understands man purely in terms of the functions he can perform will never suffer when he is compelled to judge in the realm of the incommensurable. For him there is no sweat involved in taking up a task which far exceeds all human capacity. He has his clear-cut criteria. He has too, perhaps, a conscience which is dangerously at ease. Such peace of mind is easily purchased. Indeed, it comes at first almost without one's knowing it, while one is still presumably quite innocent of what is actually going on—at the time when he steps boldly beyond the bounds of the human into the sphere of the inhuman!

But whoever suffers under the unbelievable constraint of having to judge, whoever experiences in the impossibility of his task the feeling of "metaphysical guilt," remains sound and healthy where it really counts. The wound inflicted upon him in the doing of his impossible and unavoidable task must not be allowed to heal. His pangs of conscience are a kind of gauze placed in the wound to prevent its healing in the wrong way. There are wounds—not only in the sphere of surgery but also in the domain of the human—which must not be allowed to heal. The pus of the insoluble dilemma must have some way of escaping. Otherwise, the very humanity of the physician himself becomes infected; he succumbs to the illness of illusion—particularly the illusion of the easy solution—and he warps his view of man in the direction of a naked pragmatism. On the other hand, whoever knows that in this sphere he cannot come through without taking guilt upon himself, whoever knows also the comfort of forgiveness, will find his ethos sound and healthy, immune to the temptation to press the humanum into scales of value, and thereby pervert it.

Only when this has been said and understood will one be able to have the courage—given the situation as it actually is and knowing the ambiguity of whatever he does—to go ahead anyway and seek for criteria for deciding the question of life or death in the matter of the artificial kidney. Since these criteria are, as we have indicated, questionable, necessarily alien to the meaning of human existence, the decision to which they lead can be little more than that arrived at by casting lots. The less fundamental and "metaphysical" they are, the more evident is their relativity.

For this reason the principles of selection at which we arrive in the end may well be those primitive principles already operative in American practice, for example, in the Kidney Center in Minneapolis. There is, for example, the psychological consideration of whether the strain attendent upon this kind of therapy can be endured over the years. (In this connection the treatment of children becomes impractical because too much would be demanded of them.) Then too there are economic factors to be considered, involving the patient as well as other public or private sources of funds. These and many other considerations could be decisive.

In view of the fact that such decisions always remain inconclusive, it makes sense that we not impose upon the individual physician the moral burden of deciding. Committees of specialists are set up in order to divide the responsibility. The fact that such a committee works secretly and anonymously may, on the surface, be connected with the intention of protecting its members from the direct pressures of the people seeking help. But basically this fact indicates in addition an awareness that no man is able on his own initiative, acting in his own name, to assume the responsibility for making such decisions.

More important than the procedure for arriving at such a decision, however, is the sign which points its direction. It is crucially important to keep open the wound, to preserve the ambiguity, and so to remain faithful to an awareness of that which is human.

Transplanting Organs from a Corpse

We turn now to a special aspect of the problem of organ transplants, that involving the transfer of organs from a corpse. I am referring of course to the taking of organs and tissues from a body immediately after death.[15] Like everything else we have been con-

[15] See the report of F. Gaudart d'Allaines, in *Bulletin de L'Académie Nationale de Medicine,* the session of 11 January 1966, p. 6, and the session of 10 May 1966, p. 249.

sidering, this topic too introduces the ethical-anthropological question. The ethical problem arises insofar as the question of death is unresolved: If the donor is still "alive," then to rob him would be to violate the principle of the inviolability of human life and to make of him a mere object.[16]

The difficulty with reclaiming cadaver organs results from the fact, as d'Allaines says, that "removing organs post mortem is unsatisfactory. . . . The use of transplantable organs [kidneys, heart, in the future probably also liver and lungs] becomes impossible once the blood circulation has been interrupted."[17] It could cause irreversible damage. This is true especially for the heart, which cannot tolerate an interruption of its oxygen supply. For this reason one should seek as donors individuals who are surely dying but whose life can be maintained artificially.

Among the multiplicity of medical, legal, ethical, and religious problems which this raises, one question stands out as the really critical one: What kind of life is this that is thus artificially sustained with a view to organ transplantation? Is such an individual still human? Whether or not such interventions are permissible depends on the answer to this question. In other words, what is in question is the definition of death.

Here the Académie Nationale de Médecine, as reported by d'Allaines, has described one possible path of action. It suggests that the individual be declared dead (perhaps when the encephalogram indicates the absence of any impulses) and the organ then removed, "but on the express condition that a prior decision has first been made to suspend cardiopulmonary assistance because it is now quite certain that the situation has become irreversible."

But what does this mean, to "declare dead?" The "once classical criteria" for determining death "no longer have the same meaning, since it is now possible to maintain artificially the cardiac and respiratory functions of an individual in a state of irreversible coma." Thus, in part at least he continues to live. For it is possible "in certain circumstances, through the modern techniques of resuscitation, artificially to maintain for a certain time the life of certain

[16] See Rossier, *loc. cit.*

[17] D'Allaines, *op. cit.*, 11 January 1966.

organs of an individual in an irreversible and fatal coma."[18] And these are the organs which are then available for transplanting.

As far as the nature of man is concerned, a serious question arises at this point. Does the doctor's duty to heal extend also to this kind of life maintenance? Indeed, the question must be asked from two perspectives inasmuch as (1) the irreversible coma makes healing an utter impossibility from the very outset, and (2) the maintenance procedure has in view, not the patient himself but someone else, namely, the person who is to receive the transplant.

It seems to me that one should not speak in such cases of having maintained "life." For what is really maintained is merely certain limited biological functions. To put it more pointedly, there has been a preservation of the vitality of specific organs of an unburied corpse. Quite apart from any physiological definition of death, one could say that while there may yet be these partial "relics of life," the organism as a whole has ceased to be. And now I ask myself whether this particular preservative measure differs in any fundamental way from other forms of preservation—for instance those employed by an institute of anatomy to make cadavers available for classroom use—other than in this matter of the vitality of the specimen preserved.

This special method of preservation would then have to be understood simply as another achievement of modern medicine, which knows both how to maintain an organ within an irreversible and lethal overall situation, and to make it organically productive again by means of transplantation. I see no reason why this should involve any ethical or religious problems. If we choose to speak of the "preservation of the vitality of specific organs," it is because the term suggests—as we intend—that what is involved here is not a theological question about the nature of man but a biological question not directly related to the values of the humanum.

Another question with reference to transplants is whether the doctor's concern for the recipient—or perhaps even his professional pride in his own surgical skills—might make him overly eager to suspend resuscitation efforts on the donor. Might the doctor be caught up in such a conflict of interests? It hardly takes a very fertile imagination to conceive of some highly macabre situations

[18] Ibid., 10 May 1966.

in this respect. To preclude such an eventuality the first and most decisive requirement would be that the medical team which determines the death of the donor must always be different from the one which performs the transplant. This diversification should be established by law.

THE POSSIBILITIES AND PITFALLS OF PROGRESS

We have traversed a wide terrain. We spoke of the vicious circle of medical progress, and of how the deterioration of man's hereditary material may demand as its price the acceptance of certain eugenic consequences. We spoke of limits to the physician's duty to heal in the case of forced prolongation of life. And we spoke of the insolubility of the borderline situations in which the physician finds himself when through a tragic chain of events he is called upon to be judge over life and death. Even when starting with very concrete, albeit representative, cases such as PKU mental disease or organ transplants we were repeatedly confronted with the central questions concerning the nature, destiny, and dignity of human existence. And there was hardly a dimension of man's existence on which we did not touch in one way or another. I think, for example, of the concept of identity, the meaning of pain and suffering, the nature of self-consciousness and communication, and finally the significance of such meaning-laden words as guilt and death.

The Systematic Approach

If I may be permitted to confess which of these many problems fascinates me most—perhaps with an eerie kind of fascination —I would have to mention nature's counterattack against the onslaughts of medicine. We spoke of this counterattack as the price which nature demands in return for that which has been wrested from her. For example, a higher life expectancy and other factors attributable to medical progress lead to the population explosion—particularly in areas where hunger is already a problem—and as a result the negative factor implicit in progress now demands countermeasures on the part of the very science which triggered the impulse of progress in the first place. The deterioration of hereditary substance which threatens to follow upon the increase of hereditary diseases in the stream of the generations demands in turn eugenic measures, possibly sterilization, in order to prevent that which man has created from becoming a dangerous deleterious factor. What we are confronted with here is a self-contradiction in human activity, behind which there stands a mystery which, as I have tried to suggest, demands religious interpretation.

The transitional period in which we live still denies to us in many areas any decisive solution; indeed, it hardly permits us to get much beyond feeble attempts at exploration and experimentation. The complexity and uncertainty of situations, including those involving sickness and disease, customarily lead us to restrict ourselves to treating merely the symptoms; we are satisfied merely to deal with the problems in hand, in other words, to do a patchwork job.

On the other hand, it cannot be denied that medical progress confronts us with questions of a very fundamental nature which, in the long run, cannot be dealt with piecemeal. These include questions concerning the dialectic between progress and regression, between healings effected and genetic deficiencies thereby incurred. I am assuming in this connection that specialists will readily think of a countless number of instances in which this vicious circle manifests itself. Even the triumphant success of the antibiotics has not been altogether without its melancholic side effects; it is almost as if the bacteria, with their back to the wall, had organized themselves into a resistance movement to counter the threat. This of course is only another example to illustrate this dialectic of progress and regression. It shows once again that in our world progress is not a one-way street. We spoke of the fact that for every step forward there is a price, a premium, that has to be paid. And as I see it, it is here that the decisive problems confronting us actually lie. I speak of them only with hesitation, because this virgin territory which we are about to enter is still shrouded with dense fog. The question seems to me to be as follows.

If the problems we confront have their roots in the very system of medicine as such, that is, in the dialectical relation between progress and the price to be paid for it, then in the long run one can react to these problems only in a systematic way. A succession of isolated tactical actions will not suffice; an overall strategy will have to be developed. In the attempts being made, for example, to check the population explosion, that is, in the attempts to control with the help of medicine a development which has been set in motion by medicine, we see already the rudiments of such a strategic approach. I am thinking here particularly of attempts such as those made in Japan where, with the help of legislation, preventive measures were taken with respect to an entire nation. It is conceivable that in the long run we will find it necessary to develop a similar kind of eugenics strategy on a world-wide basis.

Of course, it would be the height of arrogance for any individual, and particularly a layman, to attempt to exalt his visions of the future into serious proposals. Even though it is impossible for me to go that far, still I have my reasons for telling an audience of this sort that these global problems are approaching and that it would be good for us to prepare for them. I would like to exemplify this prognosis—better, these tasks—by means of an illustration from a completely different sphere.

For many centuries poverty was attacked piecemeal, by treating the symptoms (to put it in medical terminology). As individual cases of hunger and suffering were discovered, Christians went to their aid with alms and soups for the poor. Such loving concern was exercised not only by individuals but occasionally also by diaconic organizations. This went on until Karl Marx brought about a kind of Copernican revolution in the matter. He investigated the causes of poverty systematically and found them right in the structure of society, specifically in its capitalistic constitution. His diagnosis, which located the problem in the system itself, demanded a correspondingly systematic therapy. A paternalistically inclined factory owner who cared for his employees, kept the wolf from their door, and reached into his own purse when through no fault of their own they came upon hard times, now appeared to be downright dangerous because by his treatment of the symptoms he covered over the structurally conditioned character of the illness. An admittedly self-serving capitalist, by contrast, allowed the disease to appear much more openly; his conduct made evident exactly where the real chains of society weighed heavily.

Whether or not Marx's analysis was right need not concern us here. What is decisive is that he located the problem in the social system and reacted accordingly with systematic countermeasures: He recommended a restructuring of society. To put it figuratively, one might say that, whereas the church at that time was merely handing out umbrellas to individuals about to be inundated by the rain, Marx set out to do something about the overall weather system.

Now this is my question: Must not medicine too investigate the overall weather system? Must not medicine attempt to diagnose the ambiguity inherent in the very structure of progress, and then react with a correspondingly systematic answer? I am thinking here of an answer which we have already considered. Medicine might, for example, face up to the impending deterioration in man's hereditary substance as a result of progress and attempt to deal with it by urging the adoption of corresponding eugenic measures—for instance, by supporting legislative regulation of sterilization. Would not such an approach, by duly recognizing the dialectic of progress and its price, represent a "systematic" approach?

Atomic physics confronts us with analogous problems, and it is precisely this striking analogy which confirms my personal conviction that these questions are also addressed to the field of medicine. The physicists most acutely aware of the ambiguity of the advances their science has recently made possible for mankind are the very ones who are becoming politically concerned. They are convinced that it is not possible to deal with this ambiguity piecemeal. Nonproliferation treaties, the outlawing of atomic testing, and similar ad hoc measures afford no comprehensive and effective deterrent to the threat of self-annihilation.

The catastrophic danger to which progress in the field of nuclear power has exposed us lies again in the matter of structure. The problem is that two major powers now stand over against one another as rivals, and that as a result there is inherent within the world system itself the possibility of world destruction. Accordingly, some see the solution here too, not in piecemeal measures but in a systematic restructuring of the world which would entail the establishment of a world-state. Elimination of the various individual sovereignties would make superfluous the military forms of self-assertion, including atomic weapons. Military conflicts would thus be replaced by a kind of domestic politics on a world scale, and this in turn would be secured by means of police action.

Thus, in this sphere of life too the task is one of diagnosing and treating the system. The closely-knit interrelationships of our world compel us to see both diagnosis and therapy on a world scale.

I said that I find this analogy from atomic physics fascinating because it exemplifies the tasks which we face in the field of medicine. The analogy is significant, however, in an even deeper sense. This utopian world-state, for its part, cannot claim to be the end result of authentic progress. Neither does it imply a true self-transcendence on the part of man. Already in the medieval Antichrist plays it was depicted not as a long sought and much desired goal but as an apocalyptic terror. The emperor of the world is at the same time the antagonist of God, the Antichrist, in whom is crystallized a demonic power for which man is no match. Even in such a presumed goal of history as the world-state, then, what we have is not the desired unambiguous progress, but human ambiguity raised to the *n*th power. Huxley's "unitary system of self-government" is subject to the same ambiguity; even now it strikes us as being the dreaded ant-society, the "Big Brother" state of George Orwell.

Man's Unchangeable Identity

This observation is exceedingly significant, for here again in this analogy there emerges that which, when we noted it earlier in our discussion of the dialectical character of medical progress, plunged us into deep theological questions. To use a concept from Goethe, one could say that here we see the "limits of humanity." Here we come up against the fundamental question of man himself, the question which, no matter how much man may be able to accomplish, still keeps us humble and preserves us from utopian fantasies.

In closing, I should like to explicate these limits of humanity in terms of the assertion that man is not able to transcend himself. He is not able, either biologically (by means of hybrid breeding), or sociologically (by means of the world-state), or by any other form of intervention, to change his basic nature or get away from what he really is. As a theologian I may be permitted to express the thesis in this way: Man is and remains a sinner, in need of forgiveness and of salvation. The degree to which man always remains subject to his own ambiguity is readily suggested by two observations from the field of genetics.

First, even at the point where man attains his highest possibilities, namely, in the manipulation of his own genes, he can betray himself. The betrayal would consist in his desire to change himself and to transcend his creatureliness in order that he might be able to cope biologically with what he has created technically, and so not be left behind by apparatuses of his own devising. Precisely at the point of this supreme possibility, opened to him by progress, he would be doing violence to his own humanity. He would be surrendering that for which he was destined by creation, that he should himself be the measure of all things. He would instead be allowing himself to be ruled dictatorially by the things themselves. How paradoxical: that man should actually disenfranchise himself through the application of his own intelligence!

Make no mistake about it—that which may here seem like starry-eyed speculation has already been seriously considered in connection with space travel. In his critique of the astronautical capacities of present-day man Haldane suggests that if it were possible by means of a grafting process to build into the human hereditary mass certain traits of the gibbon (or even of a platyrhine ape with a prehensile tail), we would have a better race of astronauts.[19] Here man's commission to subdue the earth seems to have been forfeited. Indeed, the very means he had been using to fulfill that commission rise up in revolt. The means themselves become the model of what man's ends should be. They deny him the distinction of being an end in himself.

Thus, what we have here is nothing less than a betrayal of the preeminence and prerogatives of human existence. And this betrayal takes place not at the point where man descends below the level of his humanity but precisely at the point where he ascends above it. I must confess that in this connection I am reminded of the words of Jesus in which he points to the greater peril, not of such low specimens of humanity as the tax collectors and harlots but of the Pharisees and the "clever ones," those who try to transcend themselves and who, in so doing, lose all.

Second, apart from this goal of trying to cope biologically with the apparatuses he has himself made, another betrayal of humanity lies in the illusion that it is possible for man to transcend himself by means of breeding. Here one thinks to take his bearings from

[19] See J. B. S. Haldane, "Biological Possibilities for the Human Species in the Next Ten Thousand Years," *Man and His Future,* pp. 337-61, esp. p. 354; also Kaufmann, *op. cit.,* p. 116.

familiar zoological parallels, because with animals we are indeed able to make progress by means of breeding.

But the analogy immediately breaks down. For the goal of animal breeding can only be a limited one; indeed, it must of necessity be highly specialized. One can breed pigs which render better hams, or horses which run faster. But in what direction would one move in the matter of human breeding, particularly if what is sought is a totally new constitution and not just a specialized capacity to handle certain apparatuses? Would one try to eradicate Faust's restlessness, Hamlet's indecision, King Lear's pangs of conscience, Romeo and Juliet's conflicts? Would one aim at the hormone-guided dullness of homunculi, who in animal-like innocence, in an ahistorical realm beyond fear and hope, simply sit and vegetate?

Here again the betrayal takes place at the apex of human possibility. It is precisely at the point of man's supreme achievements in biology, as these now seem sooner or later to be likely of realization, that a public statement of bankruptcy may be in order. We have failed even to think about what man is, and about how certain things may be integral to his very nature—things such as fate, with which man has to wrestle; guilt, with which he must cope if he is to realize his destiny; fear, which can become creative in art and in all human enterprise; hope, which gets man moving so he can gain his future; conflict, wherein he grows towards maturity. We are so preoccupied with the question of what man "can do," that we are in danger of forgetting what he "is." We tend to forget that the very nature of man's being is such as to forbid his willing all that of which he is admittedly capable.

In connection with this public statement of bankruptcy we may recall the skeptical words of Albert Einstein: "We live in a time of perfected means and confused ends." It is no small contribution when the means delivered into our hands by progress become so perfect that they make us a bit sick—and skeptical—and cause us to inquire about the goal, the meaning, and the nature of human existence.

The Nature and Destiny of Man

I hope that what I have been saying has at least made clear this one point: The question as to the nature and destiny of man is not just a philosophical question to be dealt with at our leisure—*if* we happen to have a penchant for such lofty matters. On the contrary, it is the basic life-and-death question. We run into it whereever we go and in connection with almost all the problems we confront in the field of medicine, particularly as regards the direction of medical and biological progress.

What is man? Clearly no answer is to be had in terms of the genetic inquiry into whence he comes. Neither will the information be forthcoming in terms of the teleological inquiry into what one can do with him by way of manipulating his hereditary material. In the effort to shed light on the nature of man, the inquiry concerning his origin will always lead to his being understood as simply a higher—perhaps even the highest—animal. If, on the other hand, the criterion is some utopian end product, a biological homunculus yet to be achieved, then one can only envision the horrible specter of the superman or the lemur.

When it comes to deciding who or what man is, and whether he is to be understood in terms of his utility or in terms of his "alien dignity," science is of no help to us. We must already have made a decision on this question before we can even begin our scientific research, particularly if that research is such as will have a bearing on some dimension of human existence. Unless we have made this prior decision, unless we have faced up to the inescapable necessity for such a confession of faith—and to decide in this matter is indeed to confess one's faith—we stagger aimlessly along the road of progress as in a stupor, muttering to ourselves the wildest kind of nonsense. And the highest IQ, even the Nobel Prize, cannot protect us from ridiculous absurdities.

For the open-eyed observer, the progress of modern medicine inevitably raises the ethical question: What may we do, and what must we not do? But this ethical question immediately sparks the anthropological question concerning human identity in general, and we are confronted with the question of man: Who or what is he? Our research activity poses the question but does not answer it. Woe to him, however, who will not even hear the question, who is oblivious of ends and lets the ingenuity of the researcher take him wherever it will! With Paul one might say that wisdom of this sort amounts to sheer foolishness. One cannot give up, though, on the person who, while honestly facing the question, cannot find the answer. He at least is aware of the dilemma. And the openness of his inquiry will at least allow him to remain "human"; it will keep him from becoming an "inhuman" robot without a soul.[20]

But where shall I look for the answer to this question of human identity? You all understand, of course, that with respect to this question no answer can possibly have the same stringency and universal validity as the postulates of the exact sciences. Here one can only show his colors by declaring, as in a confession of faith, what all his experiences—of suffering, personal fulfillment, and reflection—have crystallized into firm conviction. Although to this point my arguments have been objectively formulated, I have never denied—nor would I attempt to deny—the fundamental conviction that underlies them. Hence no breach in the established pattern of my lectures is involved if here at the end I attempt to suggest the direction in which I believe we must look for this answer. I would be disappointed, however, if you were to consider what I am about to say as merely a pious appendage which I am obligated to add out of deference to my vocation. What I am attempting now is rather to make explicitly clear for a moment the conviction which has implicitly illumined all our reflections to this point.

Carlyle once threw out a challenge to a conference of natural scientists convened to discuss the origin of species: You say that man is little more than a tadpole. But I hold with the psalmist who said, "Thou hast made him little less than God (Ps. 8:5)." Note well here Carlyle's two points of reference: a little more than a tadpole . . . a little less than God! What he meant was simply this: I have nothing against the idea—even as a Christian I have nothing against the idea—that man has risen up out of the state of the tadpole. Why shouldn't he have? What I reject is the attempt to define man in terms of his origin, and hence to view human nature as a variation of tadpoleness. No. If I wish to define the nature of man, I will have to consider totally different perspectives. I will have to ask about the end for which he was created and the destiny for which he was intended by a higher hand. And it is when I begin inquiring along

[20] P. H. Rossier (*loc. cit.*) has formulated this constantly changing question concerning human identity in a thought-provoking way: "Descartes still said: 'I think, therefore I am.' With the philosophers of our time, this aphorism now reads: 'I am, therefore I think.' But the man of the future, the man made up of spare parts [*l'homme greffe*] would only be able to say: 'I am and I think, but I no longer know who I am or what I think.' "

these lines that I come smack up against that second point of reference: "a little less than God." Then I begin to understand that man stands under the patronage of an eternal benevolence, whence comes that "alien dignity" which makes him inviolable and forbids his being subjected to the dictatorial rule of his own technical capacities. Even if creation has fallen and is at odds with itself, even if within creation there is a revolt of means, a man is nonetheless called by his name and sheltered by an overarching rainbow of protection which safeguards what he "is" from all attack by what he merely "can do."

* * *

DR. RORSCHACH: Dr. Mead has told us that all of these problems associated with medical progress can be solved if we only place our trust in the medical profession. I would like to ask Dr. Thielicke the following question: Does he share Dr. Mead's trust in the medical profession, guided—as she has said—only by the oath of Hippocrates?

I am a physical scientist, and it has always been my belief that one should follow truth wherever it might lead; on the other hand, after hearing Dr. Thielicke's talk and thinking about the problems that are faced by a research worker in the field of biochemistry or in the field of medicine, I am compelled to raise the following additional questions: What is a scientist's obligation to the truth where it infringes upon humanity and how must a scientist limit himself in this area? Finally, does the biblical command to subdue the earth include any other changes we might want to make in humanity?

DR. THIELICKE: First, the question as to whether all problems can be solved by medicine: I think not, because medicine, like any other scholarly discipline, is concerned only with particular aspects of human problems. In this respect medicine is in much the same position as technology, for example. It is important for us to maintain the integrity of human existence. That is our problem. We are confronted by the fact that technically and scientifically we are more sophisticated than we are able to cope with, so that our existence is threatened by our technological capabilities. For that reason I think the most important thing we have to do is to illumine the question of human existence. We have to do that first, before we can go on to doing other things.

That leads to the second question: By what is the natural scientist bound, what are his limits? The problem becomes apparent insofar as the various views that scientists have cannot all be the basis of man's understanding of himself. There are, for instance, the Christian's understanding of the good in man, the secular understanding of the good in man, and many other understandings of man. I alluded to this somewhat in my lecture because I am convinced that you cannot assume that all the various denominations and points of view embrace one and the same understanding of man. Much more important than a unified answer to the question, however, is that this concern be maintained as a question. The tragedy of our situation lies not in the pluralism of the answers given but in the fact that, in the absence of any common Christian position, each branch of science postulates absoluteness for its particular field. For instance, the technician is increasingly in danger of believing that because he *can* do everything, he therefore *may* do everything.

The third question asked about what is implied by the biblical command. I would like to give the following answer. In this command it is stated expressly that the world is to be made subject to man, not that man is to be made subject to the world. Until now, however, we seem prone to do exactly the opposite, for we are asking whether man is psychologically and anatomically still able to keep up with what he is himself constructing. In America the question has been raised as to whether man is adapted to what he has made, for example, with regard to space travel. If now, for instance, man were to change his own structure in order to be better able to cope with the problems of space travel, then this would be contrary to the command given in the biblical account. For in such a case man is no longer the measure of things, of all those things he created; instead he becomes subject to them, and the things are then the measure of him.

DR. JUSTICE: Dr. Thielicke has expressed a critical need for man to take cognizance of what he "is" while he is pursuing the question of what he "can do." What man can do is brilliantly illustrated by his own body manipulating—by finding ways to substitute healthy parts for sick ones in his body.

Before we become overly concerned with what the advances of science and technology may mean to future man, I believe we also ought to consider a few examples of how science and technology have failed man. The failure has been so dismal in some cases that if it continues uncorrected the future of man may indeed be stormy.

The failure I'm talking about is the crisis of our cities. Although science and technology worked only too well to help produce the problem, science and technology have done little to help solve the crisis. There have been little of the countermeasures Dr. Thielicke referred to. We have no urban science; we have no urban technology. We have some people beginning to call themselves urbanologists, but if you look closely at what they do, they are much more attached to describing urban problems than to solving them.

I would like to ask Dr. Thielicke if he has any suggestions for solving the problems of nature, science, and technology so as to produce countermeasures for coping with this situation.

We have a whole host of specialists on the individual problems of our city taken separately. We have experts on crime and delinquency, on public health, education, employment, housing, transportation, welfare. Yet our cities have unprecedented crime in the streets; we still can't get help where it is needed; we still can't keep kids from dropping out of school or getting a flat nothing out of education. We still have thousands unemployed and countless others in dead-end jobs. We still have people living in slums without hot water or indoor plumbing and electricity. We don't have enough parks or available land for parks. We still have impossible problems with traffic and public transit systems. We still have an increasing welfare load and a rising number of dependent children. And we still have taxpayers who understandably complain about high taxes and revolt against taxing themselves more and more in paying for all these projects.

Money alone won't solve these problems. The solution they demand is one which not only meets the problems of the future, but which can go back and correct those in the past that have been piling up for so long. And we haven't come up with it yet.

The need exists now for countermeasures of a systemic and structural nature. We have no tools, no technology for collective problems. We can make all sorts of stupendous progress in medicine and in the ability to become supermen, but we haven't solved even the most basic problems of help for many people in the ghetto who remain in one place while all our magnificent medicine and science remain in another.

We are leaving basic lines in high school. We haven't solved the basic problems of education yet for young people of all colors and classes so that they have the skill required to make decent livings. We have raised our employment, but we haven't solved the problem of the masses of unemployed or the hard core poor, who have been lost in problems generation after generation. We have more freeways than ever—more fancy plans for getting people to and from work; but we still have city dwellers who are served by no transportation system and hardly have the price for the fare anyway.

These are not just problems of one city. They are problems of all cities. They are collective problems and we are trying to solve them with obsolete tools. I am interested in whether our failure in this field concerns ethics as well as science and technology.

Dr. Thielicke expressed at this conference the ambivalence of progress. There is no better way to find examples of this ambivalence than in the urban crisis. We have glorious skylines, breathtaking skyscrapers; millions of people have more money than they ever dreamed they would; people drive handsome cars and live in plush homes. Yet we have riots in our city. People want to know what is being done to stop riots and what is to be done to prevent the "long, hot summers." They want one-shot solutions. They want a quick-acting antidote. But there is no wonder drug for this sickness. We have just begun to diagnose the trouble and we still haven't diagnosed or found that all-purpose antibiotic for it.

I don't believe we can let these problems go unattended. I don't believe we can expect these problems to be solved by the present state of our knowledge of cities. I believe man needs a new science—a new technology to cope with it.

I am glad that we have made such progress in other fields that we need to ask where our various successes are leading us. But before we get too wrapped up in our various successes, I hope we will also consider the lack of success which characterizes the urban problem.

Dr. Thielicke has stated that man is no longer the measure of all things as much as his man-made structures, his technology and material progress are. The city is one of man's structures and one of his technological monuments. It is not functioning as it should when people are slow to awaken to any need for concern for the innumerable problems of our cities.

I submit that we are faced with an ethical question here as well as one of science and technology. But I would like to hear from Dr. Thielicke on this.

DR. THIELICKE: I would like to respond by thinking with you about the individuality and the social consciousness of the good samaritan in Luke's Gospel. Let us imagine for a moment that after he has done his good deed, this good samaritan has gone home. After all, he was not by vocation a good samaritan. He had a different job. He was something else. Perhaps he was even the mayor of his city. Now what has he done according to the parable? Was he fooling himself? If I find someone who has fallen into the hands of robbers, and these robbers did not help him, then I as the mayor —if I am really the mayor—out of love would have to conceive and devise certain ways and means of preventing other people too from falling into the hands of robbers when they walk through the forests. I would have to comb the forests in order to rid them of robbers. Now, this is the duty of Christian love, not simply to heal wounds, but to prevent their occurring. It is a question of recognition, foresight, and planning.

Indeed, it is a question of administration. You will have to be concerned with the structures of city administration. This is an illustration of the fact that Christian love is concerned not only with the individual soul, but with all of the structures that surround human life.

But this love cannot simply be identified with the structures as such. Where this happens the concern of love changes as the structures change. This is clear, for instance, in the case of political ethics: It is really impossible for us literally to translate all overtures of compassion into political objectives.

Or take the example of love and marriage. In former times one married because he or she had been pledged to another person, and love followed. Then came the time when love preceded: one began to love another because one was given by God to the other. I believe that there is no one in this group who was given to another in the former fashion. All over the world today one first loves and then marries on the basis of this love.

But we have to be aware of the fact that this unusual emphasis on the individual erotic function is a rather late innovation in western civilization. The New Testament never saw it in this way. Even since the Reformation, it has not always been seen this way. Luther, for example, saw the institution of marriage as a means of canonizing a mutual obligation affirming a divine order.

But we have arrived now at the situation where we understand the individual Eros as a means of fulfilling one's life. This new understanding then becomes something that we have to interpret through all the various phases and aspects of ethics. This means, for instance, that we must now see the individual Eros as a gift from God for which we are responsible.

I hope that I have understood the question properly. I have cited these examples in order to show that the structures of the world in which we live do change. And as they change we have to be careful not to become dogmatically stiff and rigid. If the structures change, then theology in time does have to communicate with representatives of the various disciplines concerned with man's structures of technology and politics and so on. Channels of communication need to be established in order to be able to make this dialogue possible.

In my country today there are all kinds of groups engaged in interdisciplinary dialogue. The other day I spoke at a conference of surgeons. I have participated in many meetings of industrialists and business men, who invited not only theologians but also historians and authors and representatives of other disciplines as well so that real dialogue could take place. Ever since 1945 both the Catholics and Protestants have conducted programs for making such communication possible. So far as I know, all of this is still largely on an individual and unofficial basis. I am of the opinion, however, that the more rapid planning which is called for today must grow out of such interdisciplinary dialogue; and I can envision the significance of this conference in terms of its expediting planning for the future with reference to the issues raised here.

I was very thankful for the suggestion that the large cities which we know in our western world indeed confront us with large crises. The big city in this case affords an excellent illustration. On the one hand, we see it create the conditions for making human life possible, and on the other hand we find there the abysmal and depressing aspects of big-city life.

I am of the opinion that in the future we will have to develop altogether new sciences in order to be able to solve the problems which confront us here. I hope I am not expressing undue pessimism when I say that the technology and science of the big city will not make it a heaven on earth. In the past, the city has been the glory of man. Now one sees that big-city life is terribly dehumanized. The big city consists wholly of office buildings and factories; the people often live at a great distance from the cultural centers. Now, there is a certain emotional pathology among women who linger in their beautiful country houses. There are also diseases of the inner city. I have the opinion that in coming back to the cities we must reintroduce there the human element.

I mention this in order to suggest that we stand only at the beginning of some possible solutions. It is probably important that we sustain an open and free dialogue so that we understand the big city as a beautiful example of the ambiguity of the social structures into which we are integrated.

FATHER MORACZEWSKI: I would like to make an observation, suggest a distinction, and propose a question.

The observation is that it would seem in a discussion of this nature that biology—I would also include psychology—would give us the principles and facts for determining the presence of human life, while theology will give us the principles by which we can assess the worth and meaning of human life. Hence, we must seek from biologists the basis of the distinctions between biological life and human life, distinctions such as those made in other papers involving clinical death and biological death. These distinctions appear to me to be based on an ancient biology or on pragmatic grounds. Biologically, once the zygote is formed, there is a smooth, gradual development of the individual. I know of no evidence upon which one could base a distinction that now we have merely a form of primitive life less than man; at some point we have man; and then, at the terminal stages of his life, no longer man, but something less than man. I know of no discontinuities in the development of the individual except what might be called microdiscontinuities represented by cell division. It is true that the manifestation or expression of human life at one level is more apparent at one time than at another. When a person is awake, for example, he shows human life more readily than when he is asleep or in a coma. Still, the underlying life seems to me to be the same. That is the observation.

The distinction is this: It is one thing to terminate a human life by positive action, such as removal of a heart, and another thing to terminate the life by a negative action, for example, by not giving a kidney in a case where the person's life depends on receiving a new or artificial kidney. I think this distinction is very important in some of Dr. Thielicke's issues.

Finally, the question. This question is based on two statements made by Professor Thielicke which, at first sight, seem to me to involve a contradiction. Knowing the professor, I am sure there is no real contradiction involved; hence, I would like him to comment specifically on this possibility. The first statement made earlier in the paper reads as follows: "Only what is notoriously without meaning can be abandoned to destruction." At the end of the paper he then has this second statement: "Even the most pitiful life still shares in this protection"—that is, the protection from being dispensed with. These two statements seem to be in opposition, and I would like the professor to comment on this.

DR. THIELICKE: I appreciate very much these reactions. As to the question whether even the most pitiful life is worth saving, this question must be seen in connection with that undefinable or unconditional quality of any human life which forbids our manipulating that life in any way we please. What criteria would we use for deciding which life in a mental institution we are to save and which life we are not to save? These could only be pragmatic criteria. I very clearly remember the criteria used in the Third Reich under Hitler: "These people are useless parasites, especially during time of war when there is a food shortage." Human life cannot be qualitatively evaluated, and for this reason such a protection has to exist.

There are basically two principal ways of deciding the value of human life. One is in view of a man's relation to God, that is, in relation to that which is above him; the other is in view of his relation to that which is below him. The way in which any man treats another must be evaluated in terms of these two criteria, both of which are expressed very well in literary documents, the one in Psalm 8, and the other in the chorus passages of the *Antigone* by Sophocles.

Psalm 8 says: "What is man that you remember him? You have made him just a little bit less than God." Here the relation to God is expressed.

In the *Antigone* it is just the opposite. Here it is said that there are many powerful things living, but none is more powerful than the human being. He conquered the ocean, he cultivated the primeval forests, and physicians have conquered disease. He is subject ultimately only unto death. Here the dignity of man is seen in relation to that which is below him, that from which he arises.

A little bit less than God or a little bit more than the primeval forests, the ocean, or disease. I believe that all action regarding man is decided with reference to one of these two alternatives, these ways of interpreting human life. Man is seen either in relation to that which is subject to him or in relation to God. If man is measured with reference to that which is below him, then he is measured according to his ability to function, his utility. If he is measured with reference to God, then he has about him an unimpeachable quality which cannot be violated.

BIBLIOGRAPHY

Bibliography

Barbour, Ian G. *Issues in Science and Religion.* Englewood Cliffs, N. J.: Prentice-Hall, 1966.

Bockle, Franz. *Law and Conscience.* New York: Sheed and Ward, 1967.

Bonhoeffer, Dietrich. *Ethics.* Edited by Eberhard Bethge: New York: Macmillan Co., 1955.

Breasted, J. H. *The Dawn of Conscience.* New York: Scribner, 1934.

Brown, H. *The Challenge of Man's Future.* New York: Viking, 1954.

Cabot, R. C. *Adventures on the Borderline of Ethics.* New York: Macmillan Co., 1926.

Calderone, Mary S., ed. *Abortion in the United States.* New York: Hoeber Med. Div., Harper, 1958.

Cooke, Robert E., ed. *The Terrible Choice: The Abortion Dilemma.* New York: Bantam Books, 1968.

DeVries, Egbert, ed. *Man in Community.* New York: Association, 1967.

Ficarra, B. J. *Newer Ethical Problems in Medicine and Surgery.* Westminster, Md.: Newman, 1951.

Fletcher, Joseph. *Situation Ethics: The New Morality.* Philadelphia: Westminster, 1966.

———. *Morals and Medicine.* Boston: Beacon, 1960.

———. *Moral Responsibility: Situation Ethics at Work.* Philadelphia: Westminster, 1967.

Flood, Dom Peter, ed. *New Problems in Medical Ethics.* Techny, Ill.: Divine Word Publications, 1962.

Garceau, O. "Morals of Medicine" Bibliography. *Annals of the American Academy of Medicine* 363 (January 1966): 60-69.

Garlick, Phyllis L. *Man's Search for Health: A Study in the Inter-Relation of Religion and Medicine.* London: Highway, 1952.

Glover, W. K. *Artificial Insemination Among Human Beings: Medical, Legal and Moral Aspects.* Washington: Catholic University of America, 1948.

Good, F. L., and Kelley, O. F. *Marriage, Morals and Medical Care.* New York: Kenedy, 1951.

Guttmacher, Alan F. *Life in the Making.* New York: Sun Dial, 1940.
Haggard, H. W. *Devils, Drugs and Doctors.* New York: Halcyon House Book, 1937.
Halacy, D. S. *Cyborg: Evolution of the Superman.* New York: Harper, 1965.
Huxley, Aldous. *Brave New World.* New York: Harper 1932.
Jakobovits, Rabbi. *Jewish Medical Ethics.* London: Bloch, 1962.
Jonas, Hans. *The Phenomenon of Life: Towards a Philosophical Biology.* New York: Harper, 1966.
Koestler, A. *The Act of Creation.* New York: Macmillan Co., 1964.
Koyre, Alexander. *From the Closed World to the Infinite Universe.* New York: Harper Torchbooks, 1958.
Lawrence, Lincoln. *Were We Controlled?* New Hyde Park, N.Y.: University Books, 1967.
Lehmann, Paul. *Ethics in a Christian Context.* New York: Harper, 1963.
Magoun, H. S. *The Waking Brain.* Springfield, Ill.: Charles C. Thomas, 1958.
Maslow, A. H., ed. *New Knowledge in Human Values.* New York: Harper, 1959.
Matson, F. W. *The Broken Image.* New York: Braziller, 1964.
McFadden, C. J. *Medical Ethics.* Philadelphia: Davis, 1949
McLuhan, Marshall. *Understanding Media: The Extension of Man.* New York: McGraw-Hill, 1964.
McNeill, John T. *A History of the Cure of Souls.* New York: Harper Torchbooks, 1951.
Mead, Margaret. *Anthropology: A Human Science.* New York: Van Nostrand, 1964.
———. *Growing Up in New Guinea.* New York: Morrow, 1962.
———. *Male and Female.* New York: Morrow, 1949.
———. *New Lives for Old.* New York: Morrow, 1956.
———. *Sex and Temperament in Three Primitive Societies.* New York: Apollo, 1963.
———, ed. *Cultural Patterns and Technical Change.* New York: New American Library, 1955.
Mesthene, Emmanuel George. *How Language Makes Us Know.* The Hague: Nijhoff, 1964.
———, ed. *Technology and Social Change.* New York: Bobbs-Merrill, 1967.
Mumford, Lewis. *The Myth of the Machine, Technics and Human Development.* New York: Harcourt, Brace & World, 1967.
Niebuhr, H. Richard. *The Responsible Self.* New York: Harper, 1964.

Noonan, John T. *Contraception.* Cambridge: Harvard University Press, 1965.
Noonan, John T.; Hellegers, A.; and Richardson, Herbert. *Abortion.* Cambridge: Harvard University Press, 1968.
Ramsey, Paul. *Basic Christian Ethics.* New York: Scribner, 1966.
———. *Deeds and Rules in Christian Ethics.* New York: Allenson, 1965.
———. *War and the Christian Conscience.* Durham, N.C.: Duke University Press, 1961.
———. *Who Speaks for the Church?* Nashville: Abingdon, 1967.
———, ed. *Faith and Ethics: The Theology of H. Richard Niebuhr.* New York: Harper Torchbooks, 1966.
Schmeck, H. M. *The Semi-Artificial Man.* New York: Walker & Co., 1965.
Sellers, James. *Theological Ethics.* New York: Macmillan Co., 1966.
Sharpe, W. D. *Medicine and the Ministry: A Medical Basis for Pastoral Care.* New York: Meredith, 1966.
Shaw, Russell. *Abortion on Trial.* Dayton, Ohio: P. S. Pflaum, 1968.
Simpson, G. *This View of Life.* New York: Harcourt, Brace & World, 1964.
Smith, David. *Abortion and the Law.* Cleveland: Western Reserve University Press, 1967.
Sperry, Willard. *The Ethical Basis of Medical Care.* New York: Harper, 1950.
Sonneburn, T. M., ed. *The Control of Human Heredity and Evolution.* New York: Macmillan Co., 1965.
Stevas, Norman St. John. *The Right to Life.* New York: Holt, Rinehart and Winston, Hawthorne Books, 1964.
Thielicke, Helmut. *Theological Ethics, vol. 1, Foundations.* Philadelphia: Fortress, 1966.
———. *Theological Ethics, vol. 2, Politics.* Philadelphia: Fortress, 1969.
———. *Ethics of Sex.* New York: Harper & Row, 1964.
———. *Freedom of the Christian Man.* New York: Harper, 1963.
———. *Christ and the Meaning of Life.* Edited and translated by John W. Doberstein. New York: Harper, 1962.
———. *Man in God's World.* New York: Harper, 1963.
Tournier, Paul. *The Healing of Persons.* New York: Harper, 1965.
Westermarck, Edvard. *Christianity and Morals.* New York: Macmillan Co., 1963.
White, A. D. *The History of the Warfare of Science with Theology.* New York: Dover, 1897.
Wolstenholme, Gorden E., ed. *Man and His Future: A Ciba Foundation Volume.* Boston: Little, Brown and Co., 1963.

Type, 10 on 12 and 9 on 11 Caledonia
Display, Craw and Caledonia